GALILEO AND
THE DOLPHINS

'We actually made a map of the country, on the scale
of a *mile to a mile!*'

'Have you used it much?' I enquired.

'It has never been spread out, yet,' said Mein Herr. 'The farmers
objected. They said it would cover the whole country, and shut out
the sunlight. So we now use the country itself, as its own map, and
I assure you it does nearly as well.'

Lewis Carroll, *Sylvie and Bruno*

Also by Adrian Berry

Non-fiction

The Next Ten Thousand Years
The Iron Sun
From Apes to Astronauts
The Super-Intelligent Machine
High Skies and Yellow Rain
Ice with your Evolution
Harrap's Book of Scientific Anecdotes
Eureka: A Book of Scientific Anecdotes
(Revised paperback version of the above)
The Next 500 Years

Fiction

The Fourth Reich*
The Empire in Arumac*
Koyama's Diamond
Labyrinth of Lies

Computer software

Stars and Planets
The Wedgwood Benn Machine
Kings and Queens of England
Secret Key (with Keith Malcolm)

*Under the pseudonym of Martin Hale

GALILEO AND THE DOLPHINS

Amazing but true stories
from science

ADRIAN BERRY

B T Batsford Ltd, London

To my godson Benjamin

© Adrian Berry 1996

First published 1996

The right of Adrian Berry to be identified as the author of this work
has been asserted under the Copyright, Designs and Patents Act 1988.

All black and white illustrations, except the photograph which appears with
'Pixelating Her Majesty', are the copyright of Jovan Djordjevic; tel. 0171 254 3701.

Designed & Typeset by Bernard Cavender & Greenwood Graphics Publishing
and printed in Great Britain by Biddles

Published by B T Batsford Ltd
4 Fitzhardinge Street, London W1H 0AH

A CIP catalogue for this book is available from the British Library

ISBN 0 7134 8067 X

Contents

Part Three: TOOLS FOR THE NEXT MILLENNIUM

Part Four: EDGES OF THE INFINITE

Part Five: STRANGE BELIEFS

Part Six: TEST YOUR KNOWLEDGE

Index

Acknowledgements

I am indebted to Auberon Waugh, editor of the *Literary Review*, for his kind permission to reproduce my article 'Backward Britain', which first appeared in his journal. I would also like to thank Steven Young, managing editor of *Astronomy Now*, and Pole Star Publications Ltd., for permission to reproduce several articles which I wrote as my contributions to my column in that journal.

Grateful thanks are also due to the many features editors and others at the *Daily* and *Sunday Telegraph* – and Pam Spence, editor of *Astronomy Now* – for their help in spotting errors before they could get into print: Harry Coen, Seamus Potter, Robert Cowan, Veronica Wadley, Mark Law, David Johnson, Dr Roger Highfield, and Gulshan Chunara.

I alone am responsible for any errors that remain.

Part One

IN SEARCH
OF THE PAST

Galileo and the Dolphins

A quartet of dolphins has caused amazement by rescuing a party of fishermen from shipwreck off the coast of France. The skipper called their action 'barely credible'.

The animals positioned themselves, two at the stern and two at the bows, lifted the stricken boat from the water and spent half an hour pulling it away from the rocks towards which the wind was hurling it. Their task over, they turned and swam out to sea.

The episode came as no surprise to scientists who study dolphins and regard them as serious contenders for the title of the second most intelligent mammal on the planet.

Some dolphins are trained to guard American Navy Trident submarines against frogmen saboteurs. There are well-authenticated cases of their rescuing swimmers from sharks, who are admittedly their natural enemies. Others help in treating children suffering from autism and Down's syndrome – and one dolphin became famous by falling in love with a Norwegian ferry boat.

The latter, a 13-foot lover known as Hanna, made repeated sexual passes for 10 days at the Voksa, a 150-foot car and passenger boat plying the islands off Norway's west coast. She even followed the boat into port, where she gently rubbed herself against its cold steel hull.

'There's no proof that she was really in love with the boat,' says Ken Norris, a dolphin expert retired from the University of California at Santa Cruz. 'Her amorousness may have been a pretence, to delight and amuse the passengers. Nobody knows what a dolphin is really thinking.

'Yet they can carry on complex conversations with each other by noises and bodily rhythms, and they have amazing memories. I once witnessed a group of untrained dolphins watching a complex acrobatic performance by a trained group. Three years later, without any training or rehearsal, the untrained group repeated the performance in almost exact detail.'

Mentally handicapped children are being treated, often successfully, by being taught to swim with dolphins. The psychologist David Nathanson, of the Dolphin Research Centre in Miami, believing that the main impediment to learning in these children was an inability to pay attention, thought that games with dolphins might absorb them. He was remarkably successful: one three-year-old British boy, who had failed to respond to efforts by leading speech therapists to persuade him to talk, uttered his first word. It was 'Tina', the name of the dolphin he had been playing with.

But the most extraordinary dolphin story concerns not their behaviour but politics and the history of science. It tells how a dolphin – or rather the emblem of one – is believed to have been responsible for the trial of Galileo.

This theory, propounded in the *Scientific American* of November 1986 and increasingly accepted by scientific historians, turns on a fact that has hitherto been barely credible – that a harmless 70-year-old man should have been threatened with torture and the stake merely for saying that Jupiter had moons and that the Earth orbits the Sun.

It is said that the inquisitors, obsessed with the printer's emblem of three dolphins on the title page of his *Dialogue of the Two Chief World Systems*, became convinced that Galileo was a Protestant political agent. The year was 1632. The Thirty Years War was raging and there was a paranoid

feeling among Catholic religious bureaucrats who were addicted to narrow scholasticism.

Dolphins? The very name might have been calculated to enrage them. Dolphins were associated with the shrine of the god Apollo at Delphi. In Homer's *Iliad*, Apollo was the chief divine supporter of the Trojans. One of the Trojan survivors, Francus, was the legendary founder of the French royal house. 'Dolphin' also meant 'dauphin', the heir to the French throne. France, at this time, was supporting the Protestant cause. Hence, to a Catholic, the image of a dolphin was treasonable.

We may find dolphins fascinating. In the end, Galileo's feelings are likely to have been more mixed.

Our Improbable Existence

The existence of the human race is a far more improbable event than anyone has imagined. In fact, the chances that we are here at all are about one in two billion.

A paper in *Earth and Planetary Science Letters* discloses extraordinary information about the asteroid which crashed into Earth 65 million years ago, killing the dinosaurs. It was not the impact itself that destroyed them, but the region where it happened.

For the 20-kilometre-wide object struck the Yucatan peninsula in Mexico in a place called Chicxulub, where it made a crater 300 kilometres wide under the sea – which explains how difficult it has been to find and examine the site since the first evidence for the catastrophe was found in 1980.

Chicxulub, the authors say, is an area very rich in sulphur. It is clear that the asteroid gouged out the sulphur, filling the lower atmosphere with sulphur dioxide and creating sulphuric acid haze at higher altitudes. This event, by blocking sunlight, is likely to have triggered a short Ice Age of several decades. It used to be thought that this was caused by the sheer volume of dust and soot that flew into the sky, remaining there for many years and bringing about a 'cosmic winter.' But it is now clear that this would not have happened. The dust would have fallen back to the ground within six months – too short a time for global darkness to have killed so many animals.

Instead, computer simulations suggest that the sulphuric acid particles, being lighter than dust, would have stayed in the sky for up to 30 years and created a dense haze that would have covered the planet. Throughout that time, temperatures would have dropped below zero, killing most of the plants which sustained the herbivorous dinosaurs.

'If this asteroid had struck at almost any other place on Earth,' said one of the scientists, Kevin Baines of the Jet Propulsion Laboratory at Pasadena, California, 'it wouldn't have generated the tremendous amount of sulphur that was spewed into the atmosphere to create a devastating world-wide climate change.'

Indeed, it is only because of the disappearance of the dinosaurs that we are here at all. 'We human beings owe our existence to the uniqueness of this impact region,' Baines said. For, while flesh-eating dinosaurs roamed the planet, it was impossible for our ape-like ancestors to evolve. To be intelligent, animals must reach a certain size – and long before reaching it we would all have been eaten.

Now sulphur is a comparatively rare element. It is only the ninth most abundant in the universe, and a mere 0.06 per cent of the Earth's crust is made of it. Consider, therefore, the extinction of the dinosaurs in the light of statistical probability.

Nobody knows how often a 20-kilometre-wide asteroid is likely to strike the planet, but an estimate of once in 100 million years might be reasonable. Let us say that if one does strike, the chances of it hitting a sulphurous region are quite long. Baines estimates that these might be one in twenty.

Sulphur deposits are not caused by volcanic activity as many people imagine, but by long-dead life which leaves traces of calcium sulphate. It is estimated that only a twentieth of the Earth's 500-million-square-kilometre surface, whether land or sea, has such deposits. Therefore, to calculate the chances of a sulphurous cosmic winter, we multiply one in 100 million by one in twenty. From this we see that the odds on it happening are about one in two billion.

If this particular asteroid had not struck Chicxulub, would there be any intelligent life on the planet? Some science-fiction writers have speculated that various sub-species of the dinosaurs themselves might have evolved to the extent that they could have mastered high technology. But this appears doubtful. If they were capable of such advances, why did they not show that ability during their 140 million years of existence?

The improbability of Chicxulub-type events may also help to explain why we have found no signs of intelligent life in our Milky Way galaxy. Nobody knows what the chances are of dinosaurs coming into existence, but if the chances of their subsequent extinction are very low, then it becomes extremely unlikely that intelligence will have emerged on alien planets that are otherwise congenial to life. We are very fortunate animals.

A Divine Scam

A unique scandal has been uncovered. Two senior civil servants embezzled a huge fortune, bribed other functionaries and undertook vast secret construction works. Nothing so odd in that, you may think – except for their aim. They wanted to make themselves gods.

This extraordinary scam to hijack divinity happened in ancient Egypt some 4,000 years ago, according to a team of archaeologists who have found the evidence among the pyramids of Saqqara.

The plan of the two miscreants was simple and, as far as they can ever have known in this life, entirely successful. Afterwards, however, it may have been another matter . . .

According to the Egyptian state religion, dead pharaohs automatically became gods. This was because any bodies that lay in the royal tomb were assumed by visiting spirits to be royal and were at once promoted to divine status. The two officials, senior priests named Ihy and Hetep, were responsible for 'servicing', or guarding, the divinity of the pharaoh Teti (2325–2310 BC) who had died and been deified several centuries before.

With great stealth, they began constructing their own tombs within the precincts of Teti's royal tomb. They did not go so far as to built their own pyramids – that would have made the matter too obvious. But they apparently stole the gifts which worshippers brought to Teti's tomb and bartered them to employ quarry-workers and decorators to build their own tombs and a secret corridor leading to them.

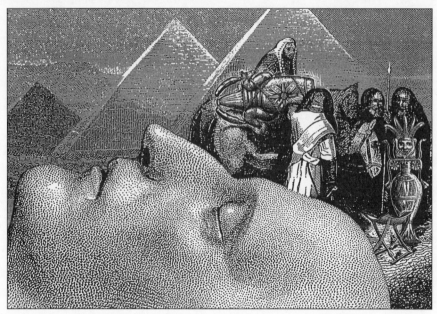

Egyptian experts have never made a discovery like this before. There have been cases of would-be gods trying to deceive the spirits by carving their own names on other peoples' tombs, but faking one's own tomb is a case without precedent.

The desire to enjoy a royal Egyptian afterlife was very different from our familiar 'burial snobbery' in which prominent people 'pull strings' to secure their interment in Westminster Abbey. Ihy and Hetep did not want everlasting fame in this world but everlasting pleasure in the next.

'Every Egyptian expected a reasonably comfortable afterlife, but the afterlife of a king was beyond anyone's wildest dreams in splendour and luxury,' said one of the archaeologists, Rita Freed of the Museum of Fine Arts in Boston. 'It was one of perpetual feasting and love-making, or whatever else you had most enjoyed while you were alive. But you never got indigestion or a hangover or a disease. You never got old and you never got fat.

'You might enjoy the glorious role of a warrior in battle, like Osiris in his struggles with his brother Seth. But you were never killed or wounded, and your image was always heroic, leading the charge or slaying dozens of enemies single-handed. You were always winning.'

But the life of an Egyptian super-god did have one drawback, said David Silverman, a museum curator at the University of Pennsylvania in Philadelphia. 'It could come to a stop at any time if the priests in this world stopped worshipping you.

'This happened in two cases. The pharaoh Akhnaton (1353–1335 BC), and Queen Hatshetsup (1473–1458 BC) were both considered after their deaths to have disgraced the monarchy. Akhnaton introduced Sun-worship and tried to abolish all Egypt's other gods, while the successors of poor Hatshetsup decreed that she should never have reigned at all because she was a woman. Worship of these two gods was officially stopped, and they thereupon ceased to be gods.'

Similarly, Ihy and Hetep would have had the 'plug pulled' on them. They made one fatal but unavoidable error. The assistants whom they employed to build their corridor and the tombs, and to make copies of the 'royal texts' to place in the tombs (to deceive the god-seeking spirits), had to know the whole story.

The two men might have been wise to have had all of them assassinated, but they could not do this, for *who otherwise would carry out their burials*? The result, Freed believes, was what might have been expected. The would-be gods behind the 'sting' were themselves posthumously stung. The assistants, knowing the whereabouts of the tombs, plundered them as soon as their masters were dead.

In this 'gangsters in wonderland' mythology, the two newly divine conspirators, together with Teti their long-dead lord, would have been deprived of the fruits of worship and instantly undeified.

The Trees that Killed

Tall evergreen trees, generally viewed as benevolent protectors against winter avalanches in the mountains and an agreeable part of nature, were once 'killers' – responsible for repeated mass extinctions that wiped out most life on the planet.

This happened during the Devonian period – named after the unique character of fossils and rocks first found in what is now Devon and Cornwall – that lasted between 400 million and 350 million years ago.

The history of Earth is filled with mass extinctions, when all or most animals suddenly vanished. The best known of these is the destruction of the dinosaurs by the impact of a giant asteroid or comet 65 million years ago.

But there were many earlier ones hitherto wrapped in mystery which do not seem to have had any such violent cause. It is almost as if a giant invisible hand had descended from the skies or risen from the depths and extinguished our primordial ancestors, leaving behind no clue to its nature.

The Devonian period came long before the reign of the dinosaurs which were not to appear for another 100 million years. But the great 'radiation explosion' of life of the Cambrian period 500 million years ago had filled the seas with coral and a vast profusion of other primitive marine creatures.

The world was very different from today. The Moon was closer than it is now, making the Earth rotate so fast that days lasted about 21 hours, with each year thus lasting about 400 days – a fact that significantly increased the rate of land erosion.

Europe and North America had collided. The consequent upthrust of mountains, which were also expanded by frequent volcanic eruptions, caused a great swelling of ocean waters that covered 85 per cent of the planet, compared with only 70 per cent today. The cause of the Devonian 'crises', which according to the *New Scientist* recurred eight times, was the evolution on land of tall evergreen trees, the first ancestors of today's pines, spruces, firs and larches. They proliferated on the shores of the huge oceans and above the banks of the rivers that flowed into them.

'The trouble came when they evolved from small creeping plants to tall trees,' said Thomas Algeo, a geochemist at the University of Cincinnati in Ohio. 'Their roots spread deeply and colonized previously barren areas. They did not have the stabilizing influence on the soil that tree roots do today. The more deeply the roots delved into the ground, the more they broke up the surface and its rocks, making the soil more vulnerable to weathering and erosion.'

Rainfall brought innumerable landslides. Soil particles and dissolved nutrients poured down the hillsides, washing

into the rivers and oceans, where they caused an explosive growth of marine algae and bacteria.

When these organisms died, their decomposition used up the oxygen in the deeper oceans and the marine animals literally suffocated. This theory fits well with all that is known about the evolution and spread of primordial conifer trees.

Each extinction was followed by a population explosion of trees which led to the next extinction. Algeo also points to black shale rocks, which were formed during the Devonian epoch and which are filled with algal material.

But were these and later mass extinctions a disaster or a blessing? Did they delay or advance the coming of intelligent life? Algeo is convinced of the latter case. 'Every time you have a mass extinction, it enables new life to spread, replacing the habitats of the old. The trees themselves which had caused the extinctions spread inland, causing more lush plant life to colonize the barren lands and appear all over the planet. This in turn created an environment in which large land animals could eventually exist.'

As for the much later extinction of the dinosaurs, that in turn made possible the coming of man (see Our Improbable Existence, p. 14), enabling our primate ancestors to fill the void they had vacated.

We have every reason to be grateful for the conifers that now fill Earth's cold and mountainous regions with their melancholy beauty.

The First Grand Nationals

Horse racing fans may not be aware that the sport was taking place at least four thousand years ago, when the ancestors of Europeans built the first chariots.

Even certain modern phrases like the 'turning point', were first coined in the chariot races of these people who spoke the ancestor of most European languages. Known as the Sintashta-Petrovka people, after the area in Kazakhstan where many of their remains were found, they became so successful that their descendants came to dominate both Europe and Asia.* Accounts of their exploits and legends survive in the Sanskrit Vedas written a thousand years later and which still survive as sacred texts in modern India.

They gave their chariots a semi-divine status, burying them with their dead owners. Examination of a tomb containing the remains of a chariot in Sintashta-Petrovka shows that these early charioteers were the same people who first rode on horseback.

The chariot races of these nomads of the vast grassy plains that lie between Mongolia and the Carpathians are recounted in detail in the sacred text called the *Rig Veda*. They raced their chariots for many purposes. Sport may have been the least important of them. Others included the settling of legal disputes, deciding the guilt of an accused

---

*Today, one of the men most hated in this region is the former Soviet dictator Nikita Khruschev, who ordered the destruction of the descendants of these horses 'to be made into sausages'. 'In Central Asia, a Desert Horse Gallops Back from Soviet Abyss', *International Herald Tribune*, November 11–12, 1995.

person, and conducting funerals. An example from later history is the chariot race described in the *Iliad* that was held at the funeral of Achilles.

But most important, their chariots revolutionized war. Until the invention of the short bow, easily drawn and discharged by a galloping horseman, the chariot was the ideal military vehicle. 'A standing warrior in a chariot could shoot arrows with a large bow or cast spears, coming very close to his target before dashing away,' said David Anthony, an archaeologist at Hartwick College at Oneonta, New York.

He has performed dating tests on grave sites which show that these chariots existed in Kazakhstan at least two centuries before they appeared in the Middle East. 'They were invented in the steppes of Eurasia by people who were, comparatively speaking, barbarians,' said Anthony.

The only sign of modern habits was their addiction to gambling. They used to throw hazel-nuts as dice. In the *Rig Veda* there is a lament of a gambler who cannot give up the habit even though his wife has left him in disgust.

For a thousand years the chariot was the superior military weapon. It later made possible the victories of the Hittites, the Egyptians and Myceneans. Only in the first millennium BC was it succeeded by cavalry.

The mastery of the horse and the invention of chariots brought one of the most important developments in human history, turning man from 'slave' to animals faster and stronger than himself into their 'king'. Evidence of this achievement has come also from the examination of horses' teeth at the prehistoric hamlet of Dereivka, 200 kilometres south of Kiev. The bones of a stallion aged seven or eight were found with a fragment of a deer's antlers that had clearly been used as a bit with a leather strap as reins. Microscopic examination of its premolar teeth showed the horse's mouth had been worn away by a bit.

Horses and chariots brought a revolution in virtually every aspect of the lives of primitive Europeans, since riders could travel across the grasslands three times further and faster in a day than people on foot. The people of Sintashta-Petrovka were so pleased with their invention that they appear to have worshipped either their horses or a god with the head of a horse.

The *Rig Veda* describes how two divine twins cut off a priest's head and replaced it with that of a dead horse. The priest then spoke through the horse's head. Scenes like this appear to have actually happened. When Anthony examined a grave site he found that it contained the remains of a human sacrifice, the victim's head having been replaced with that of a horse.

But the cavalry who replaced the charioteers in about a thousand BC cannot have enjoyed the change. For it was not until the fourth century AD, with the coming of the Huns out of Asia, that stirrups were first introduced in the West. Riding a stirrupless horse must have been far less comfortable than standing up in a chariot.

The Man who Found Cod – but not Japan

To mark the 500th anniversary of the first voyage of
John Cabot, Britain's pioneering explorer of the
Americas, an almost exact replica of his ship, the
Matthew, will sail from Bristol to duplicate his journey.

Cabot's voyage deserves this commemoration – there
have only been similar duplications in modern times of the
first voyage of Columbus and that of the *Mayflower* –
because of his role in Anglo-American history. But for
Cabot, whose English successors explored and colonized
much of the North American continent, those vast lands
might otherwise have gone to Spain, with incalculable consequences for the human race.

Cabot is believed to have been an ancestor of the famous
Massachusetts family whose aristocratic roots inspired the
verse:

> *And this is good old Boston,*
> *The land of the bean and the cod,*
> *Where the Lowells talk only to Cabots,*
> *And the Cabots talk only to God.*

The modern replica of the *Matthew* that sails in 1997, part
of the International Festival of the Sea and sponsored by the
property company Helical Bar, will not be entirely identical
to the original. It will have toilets and showers, which Cabot
and his 17 crew members of course lacked. It will also have
a twentieth-century galley.

The modern crew will all be non-smokers – which is appropriate since tobacco had not been discovered at the time of the original voyage; and, to comply with maritime safety laws, it will have radio and an engine for use in emergencies. But there will be no bunks, and the paid crew, still not chosen, must bring their own mattresses and sleep on the floor.

The story of Giovanni Caboto, a citizen of Venice, is a fascinating one. As a young man he visited Mecca, which was then not only a place of pilgrimage but the world's greatest market for the exchange of goods between East and West. Asking where the eastern spices, perfumes, silks and precious stones came from, he learned that they were from the north-eastern parts of furthest Asia. He instantly resolved that rather than pay the exorbitant prices in this market, Europeans must sail to Asia and trade directly. Like Columbus he decided the best route would be to sail *west*. And he would show Europe the way.

Rejected by Spain and Portugal, he anglicized his name and successfully sought support from England's King Henry VII, who gave him letters patent to 'seek out whatsoever isles, countries, regions or provinces of the heathen and infidels which before this time have been unknown to all Christians', and claim them for the Crown. The King was to get a fifth of the profits, and Cabot the rest.

Setting off in May, 1497, the *Matthew* reached Newfoundland after 52 days at sea and, like Columbus five years earlier, Cabot was convinced that he had reached Asia. But his only useful discovery was that of the riches of the seas off the Grand Banks. His crew caught innumerable cod simply by lowering baskets into the water and lifting them up again.

Cabot found many new islands which he claimed for England, but was baffled by the absence of an oriental civilization in Newfoundland. The natives seemed much too primitive to have produced the exquisite goods he had seen in Mecca.

He undertook a second voyage, in 1498 – the King was delighted by the first, and this time paid for six ships. Cabot had been told by a certain Jöao Ilavrador that the country known as Greenland was in fact part of Asia. If he sailed north-west of it towards the icy regions, so Ilavrador said, he would come to the wealthy kingdom of Japan. But his passage was ever more thickly obstructed by icebergs. His fellow-captains threatened to mutiny, and Cabot meekly agreed to return.

This showed the one flaw in his character that prevented him from becoming one of the greatest explorers, a lack of the ruthlessness shown later by both Magellan and Francis Drake: when Magellan faced a similar mutiny he invited the two ringleaders to his ship to discuss the matters in dispute. He then beheaded one and marooned the other.

Indeed, the only immediately tangible achievement of Cabot's second voyage was the naming of Labrador. The name came from his ill-informed adviser, Jöao Ilavrador.

The Other Big Bang

R emarkable, perhaps ominous, discoveries are being made about the other Big Bang, not the event in physics that started the Universe, but the Big Bang of biology that very suddenly created advanced animals, including our own ancestors, some 500 million years ago.

Those who imagine that civilizations in the galaxy are commonplace might do well to contemplate the meagre story of life on Earth. Not only was the planet devoid of intelligent life for 99.9 per cent of its history, it was also empty of any life more advanced than the primordial for nearly 90 per cent of this time. This hardly encourages the view that future interstellar explorers are likely to find Klingons whenever they approach a habitable planet circling a Sun-like star.

From the time of the first appearance of life some 4 billion years ago to the coming of complex life in the Cambrian age, there was a lull of 3.5 billion years during which, biologically, nothing interesting happened. Although Earth was the right distance from the Sun for life to form on it, a visiting alien spacecraft, unless its astronauts had gone searching among the rocks, would have encountered nothing, concluding no doubt that all their theories about the omnipresence of advanced creatures were wrong.

The biological Big Bang was apparently a very sudden event, quite unlike the gradual changes over periods of countless millions of years that Charles Darwin envisaged. All the experts on the subject are now in agreement that the

Cambrian 'radiation' of advanced life started exactly 543 million years ago. Before that time there was only primitive life; and immediately after it came the first complex animals.

The key to the Cambrian 'explosion' lay in the geological period that immediately preceded it, the Vendian. It was then that oxygen began to appear in enormous quantities in the oceans, created, apparently, by tremendous tectonic upheavals that caused carbon compounds to break up into oxygen and carbon. Only with oxygen could animals develop many cells and grow large. But no cause has yet been found for the Vendian tectonic upheavals. As far as we can tell they just happened; and they are responsible for one of the three great mysteries of Earth's history.

The first of these is why primitive life appeared in the first place. The second is the Cambrian explosion, and the third is the much later appearance of intelligence. Without these events we would not exist. But because of those uneventful 3.5 billion years, there is a case for arguing that the second, at least, was very unlikely to occur and without it, there could have been no question of the third, making a powerful case for suggesting that advanced intelligent planetary life must be extremely rare.

And so, to Enrico Fermi's famous rhetorical question about alien civilizations in the Milky Way – 'Where are they?' – we have an answer: they never made it to the animal stage. Yet this may not be entirely bad news. With no aliens to oppose us, the galaxy will be ours for the taking.

A Monster that Liked Treasure

The gryphons, one of the most fearsome of mythical animals, may actually have existed. Its true identity is likely to have been Titanis, a 'giant bird' that once roamed the world, terrorizing lesser creatures.

First, the legend. Herodotus, in his histories, says that in Scythia – a Crimean region – here was once a tribe called the Arimaspians whose people had only one eye.

These people were at constant war with gryphons, or 'griffins', huge animals with the heads of eagles and the bodies of lions. Their warfare was fiscal as well as physical. The gryphons had a great love for gold and precious stones with which Scythia abounded. Whenever the Arimaspians approached, hoping to lay hands on it, the gryphons would leap on them and tear them to pieces.

Stories of treasure guarded by dangerous and supposedly mythical animals are common in ancient legend, and Herodotus, never reluctant to tell a good story, may have been drawing on folk memories. Hercules, for his eleventh labour, had to kill the dragons that guarded the golden apples in the Garden of Hesperides. And the dragon Smaug, in Tolkien's *The Hobbit*, was always most comfortable when dozing on a pile of stolen treasure. The gryphon legend may have originated with the Titanis guarding its 'treasure', this being its young or eggs.

'Herodotus's description of the gryphon sounds exactly like the scientific description of Titanis,' says the British scholar George Clive. 'From its agility, its lion-like limbs and its ferocity, there is a strong case for believing it was the same animal.'

The discovery of Titanis's beak has enabled the animal to be reconstructed. Larry Marshall of the Institute of Human Origins in Berkeley, California, calls it the 'most dangerous bird that ever existed'. It was a flightless, ostrich-like creature that would strike down its prey with its gigantic talons, ripping victims apart with its hooked beak. Originating millions of years ago in South America, it was far more lethal than the peaceful ostrich it resembles. It was too heavy to fly with its feeble wings, but more than made up for this with terrific speed. Standing some four metres high, it could run faster than a horse and eat any animal it could catch. There must have been few mammals that could resist its attacks.

It even preyed on the gigantic armadillo-like mammals called glyptodons, which appeared to have no other natural enemies. Titanis's only living descendant is a three-foot-tall, long-necked bird called Cariama, found in the forests of Paraguay. Like its much larger ancestor, it can also run at up to 40 kilometres per hour.

How Titanis migrated to North America, and then to Asia, where the Arimaspians supposedly encountered it, is part of a great geological drama of natural land-bridges that once crossed ancient seas. But for these the Earth would be far less rich in animal species.

About three million years ago, volcanic forces lifted the region of the Andes mountains that crosses Venezuela; and the two continents of North and South America, hitherto islands, were joined by the new land-bridge of Panama. Hundreds of large animal species were thus able to cross it and mingle in the now-united continent. Then, during the last Ice Age, a new bridge arose across the Bering Sea which separates Siberia from Alaska.

Falling water-levels exposed long-submerged land, enabling vast numbers of animals to migrate to Asia. The ancestors of the black bear, the porcupine, the armadillo, the ant-eater, the horse, the coyote, the llama, the wolf, and the terrible Titanis, crossed.

Humans were fully evolved at this time, telling many an awesome tale over their camp fires, which is how the story of the gryphon would have come down through the ages.

The extinct Titanis-gryphon is in a sense very much alive. Its fierce, beak-like head adorns heraldry. In the seventeeth century, the heraldic expert Sir Thomas Browne wrote in his *Pseudodoxia Empidemica*: 'The griffin is an emblem of valour and magnanimity, as being composed of the eagle and the lion, the noblest animals in their kinds; and so it is applicable unto princes, presidents, generals and all heroic commanders; so it is also born in the coat-arms of many noble families of Europe.'

The real-life gryphon, however, was very different from the witty fellow who told Alice that shoes under the sea are made from 'soles and eels'.

Edmond Halley, 'Pirate in the Pink'

One day in 1700 a fishing vessel was at work off the Newfoundland coast when a ragged-looking craft bore down on it. Fearing piracy, the fisherman opened fire. The result was a torrent of foul language from the 'pirates'' commander, the astronomer Edmond Halley.

Halley was not only famous for predicting the appearance of his comet. He was also a bold explorer, travelling the world in search of scientific information, who nearly lost his life trying to find Antarctica a century before Captain Cook arrived.

His extraordinary exploits are revealed in *Astronomy Now* by the scientific historian Ian Seymour, who relates that Halley was not only a precursor of Cook but, in being faced with a mutiny that he himself partly provoked, of Captain Bligh too.

In his second voyage, begun in 1698, he set out in a Royal Naval vessel called the *Paramour Pink*. 'Pinks', flat-bottomed ships 16 metres long and 5 metres broad, specially designed for sailing in shallow seas and almost unknown in the Navy, were often mistaken for pirates sailing under false colours.

The crew numbered 20, making the vessel extremely cramped, and the first officer, a certain Harrison (no relation to the inventor of the marine chronometer) was a professional seaman who despised the 'academic' Halley from whom, he complained with gross unfairness, 'much is expected and little or nothing appears'.

During this voyage Halley did in fact make extensive observations of the Earth's magnetic fields which, Seymour says, 'remained indispensable shipboard companions for more than a century'. But he was an appallingly bad commander. Despite his naval authority, he never had a man flogged and instead attempted to enforce discipline with sarcastic and foul-mouthed abuse.

Harrison, openly insubordinate, countermanded orders and told the crew that Halley had only been given command because of his wealthy connections, since he was useless for any other occupation. One day Harrison told Halley in the presence of all the crew that he was 'not only uncapable to take charge of a Pink, but even of a longboat'. Halley had him confined to his cabin for the rest of the voyage. At the subsequent court martial the Admiralty appeared to recognize Halley's faults, for the mutinous officer escaped with only a reprimand.

On a subsequent voyage in a Pink, this time with a more agreeable first officer, Halley put in at Recife, Brazil, where he fell foul of the English consul, a Mr Hardwicke, whom he afterwards alleged was an imposter. He told Hardwicke that the purpose of the voyage was to observe the stars in the southern skies. (Halley, in fact, had earlier won election to the Royal Society for identifying 341 southern stars from the murky skies of Saint Helena.) Hardwicke said this story was too ridiculous to be believed. Citing the suspicious appearance of Halley's ship, he ordered him to be arrested as a pirate. Halley was released after a few hours at the intervention of the city's governor but, incensed and refusing to accept apologies, he set off into stormy seas.

He was soon in the Southern Ocean hoping to find the fabled Lost Continent. The ship's lookouts reported seeing three large islands, unmarked on any map. They were all 'flat at the top, covered with snow, milk-white, with perpendicular cliffs all around them'.

Surrounded by these icebergs and by thick fog, the ship was soon in deadly peril. For 'between 11 and 12 days', Halley wrote in the log, 'we were in imminent danger of the inevitable loss of all of us in case we starved, being alone without a consort.' They were saved by the smallness of the ship, which made it responsive to controls, and by its shallow draft.

Halley, who lived to 86, was one of the most remarkable scientists of all ages. A friend of Isaac Newton – probably the only friend that cantankerous man ever had – he was influential in securing the publication of his *Principia*, that basis of all celestial laws. He also discovered the first known globular cluster whose ancient stars today defy our attempts to age the universe.

And he was a great character too, as shown by his entertainment, when Astronomer Royal, of the visiting Russian tsar Peter the Great. They ended up drunk in a ditch.

Chimps Like Us

Humans are not the only animals that engage in war, politics and medical research. Chimpanzees have been known to do these too.

'When I first started studying them I thought they were nicer than we are,' says the veteran chimpanzee expert Jane Goodall. 'But time has revealed that they can be just as awful.'

In some 30 years of watching chimpanzees – our closest cousins – at Tanzania's 50-square-kilometre Gombe National Park, Goodall (whose life-story appeared in the *National Geographic*) has witnessed such phenomena as the Four-Year War, in which two rival tribes of chimps systematically stalked and slaughtered each other.

What most astonished her in this conflict, in which more than ten adults and all their young lost their lives, was its stealthy professionalism. (It was apparently aimed at taking vengeance on animals who were 'traitors', who had deserted one tribe and joined the other.) Warriors carrying out an attack or preparing for an ambush would move through the forest in single file, their hair bristling with fear and excitement, stepping from stone to stone to avoid making any tell-tale rustling sound. Then, when battle was joined, the two armies would tear at each others' flesh with their teeth.

But they used no other weapons. Military technology is one of the few areas in which chimpanzees have failed to make human-like progress. Goodall and her colleagues have observed striking traits of chimp behaviour:

Clothing. They have learned to use twigs as 'sandals' to protect their feet from thorns.

Using man-made objects for political propaganda. One diminutive chimp called Mike bluffed his way to the leadership of his group by banging kerosene cans together to create noisy displays and increase his own importance.

Psychology. A group ruler called Faben had a brother named Figan. When Faben disappeared, Figan began to imitate the behaviour and body language of his vanished brother to persuade others that their personalities were identical. By doing this, he successfully won the leadership of his group and held it for ten years.

Medicine. Some chimpanzees swallow the leaves of Aspilia, a plant that relieves stomach pains and kills internal parasites.

Tool-making. They pare down blades of thick grass and poke them into termites' nests to trick the insects into coming out to be seized and eaten.

Awe and wonder. They perform a ritual dance in front of a high waterfall, apparently displaying the emotions that may have led early humans to religion.

Marriage. A male and female, Evered and Winkle, lived alone in order to raise their own offspring. Throughout their lives they showed clear knowledge that their son Wilkie was theirs.

Being obnoxious. A 'spoiled brat' of a chimp named Frodo kicked a reporter down a hillside, seized Goodall by the ankle and pulled her to the ground, pushed a photographer over on top of her, and walked off, grinning.

None of this should surprise us since 98 per cent of the genetic material of chimpanzees is identical to ours, a far higher proportion than in any other species. Indeed, it was only six million years ago, the merest blink of an eye in the age-long history of mammals, that man and chimpanzee shared a common ancestor.

But how did this ancestor become an ancestor of such able descendants? Reports in *Nature* have identified the first known of the great apes that crossed the all-important gulf between walking on four legs and walking on two. An ape that lived nine million years ago called Dryopithicus laietanus appears to have learned to swing on branches and rush through the forests in Tarzan-like fashion, a habit still enjoyed by tree-climbing children and circus acrobats.

'It was long believed that all the great apes went through this vital intermediate phase,' said one of the scientists, Peter Andrews, of London's Natural History Museum, 'but this, from the examination of a fossil found in Spain, was the first proof of it.'

Clever ape-like behaviour suggests that it was not for nothing that the phrase 'to monkey with' originally meant adding water to milk and selling it as pure milk.

Faking the Shroud . . .

As radiological tests proceeded in 1988 to determine, once and for all, whether the Turin Shroud was genuine or faked, the enquirers were 'scooped' by an unofficial group who presented 'overwhelming evidence' that it was a forgery by an unknown fourteenth-century French artist.

Joe Nickell, a teacher, a former magician and a member of the famous Committee for the Scientific Investigation of Claims of the Paranormal, which has exposed countless frauds, set out to examine the complaint made in 1389 by a French bishop to Pope Clement VII that an artist in his diocese had 'falsely and deceitfully procured for his church a certain cloth, upon which, by clever sleight of hand, was cunningly depicted the image of a man that he falsely pretended was the actual shroud in which Our Saviour was enfolded in the tomb'. In the light of a further statement from the bishop that the unnamed forger had confessed, Nickell decided that the best way to discover how the supposed forgery could have been committed was to attempt one himself.

He was struck by the fact that the image of Christ in the Shroud is no ordinary painting but is similar to a photographic negative, in the sense that its prominences are dark and the recesses are light. Believers say this is due to a burst of energy that accompanied the Resurrection, but Nickell wondered if it had been created by a technique similar to brass-rubbing, the oldest form of printmaking. This creates negative images as in the Shroud.

'Artists in the fourteenth century were skilled in creating negative images,' said Nickell, 'and I set out to imitate their methods, being careful to use only materials and techniques that were available to them.'

He started experimenting with a bas-relief of Durer's Praying Hands, coating them with a moist rouge paint. It made a good negative image, not dissimilar to that of the Shroud, but the edges were too sharp. The moist rouge coating also had the disadvantage of preventing him from seeing the image as it formed. And he was sure the original artist would have liked to see what he was doing.

'And so, instead of moist rouge, I tried a mixture of myrrh and aloes. But my final choice was some powdered pigment made of iron oxide which is consistent with the findings of the latest microscopic tests on the Shroud. I started by creating a bas-relief of Christ's features which one of our team had made from plaster. I then took a wet cloth and moulded it over the bas-relief, taking care to remove any wrinkles.'

After allowing the cloth to dry, he used a dauber to rub this pigment into the cloth. He thus obtained on the cloth an image which, in the words of a critic, was 'identical, to all practical purposes, to that of the Shroud'.

Nickell believes there are many other vital aspects of the Shroud that prove beyond doubt that it was a medieval forgery. The strongest one is the blood, evidently painted on after the image was formed. 'The blood is red, and it shouldn't be. It should be black. Blood blackens very soon after it has been shed.'

Another discrepancy about the blood has been pointed out by one of his team, Michael Baden, a former chief medical examiner, who had examined many a corpse; that blood does not flow in neat little rivulets down the body, as it does in the Shroud. It matts and blackens. But there is nothing of this in the Shroud. It is all so artificial and artistic, not like the injuries to a real corpse.

'The blood itself on the Shroud has been subjected to forensic chemical tests,' Nickell pointed out, 'and a very odd thing was discovered. It was found to contain traces of red ochre paint, which was widely used by artists in the Middle Ages, but would cause lethal mercury poisoning if it ever found its way into a human bloodstream.'

Proponents of the genuineness of the Shroud say that it probably at one time hung under a giant fresco ceiling which dripped paint on it. But where and when they cannot say. Nickell found that a 'very ingenuous explanation. The Shroud is supposed to have received its image by being wrapped around Christ's head. But if one does that to a real, three-dimensional head – as opposed to a flat bas-relief – the laws of geometry predict that you will get distortions. You should have a grotesquely distorted face. But instead we have this flat image. It is absolutely inconsistent with the image I obtained with my experiment.'

But Nickell and his team believe the most devastating evidence of all is the 1,300-year gap between the time the Shroud was supposedly created and when it was first heard of.

'One would have supposed that this holiest of relics would have been known throughout Christendom. But for more than a thousand years it was unknown. St Augustine used to lament that no one knew what Christ looked like. In the early Middle Ages, artists painted Christ like a clean-shaven, Apollo-like youth. Then in the thirteenth and fourteenth centuries he – in the eyes of artists – took on precisely the venerable appearance that he has in the Shroud.'

Even if we discount the fact that the fourteenth century was a time of widespread forged holy relics – no less than three churches claimed to have the corpse of Mary Magdalene at the same time – the theory that the Shroud was a forgery of that century accounts for all the known evidence.

. . . And Faking the Aliens

Many will have seen film footage showing the supposed autopsy of an alien visitor to Earth – the so-called 'Roswell incident' – all those who saw it, who possessed any sense, knew it must be a fake. But the most interesting question, not answered until now, was *how* it could have been faked.

Now this ignorance is at an end. Two fascinating reports in *Skeptical Inquirer*, the bimonthly scourge of hoaxers and fakers, show exactly how it could have been done and how, if their authors had been at work, the 'alien' could have been considerably more convincing.*

The background to this piece of UFO folklore is well known. At Roswell, New Mexico, in July, 1947, there was some kind of aerial accident. Probably a military surveillance plane crashed, and the US government naturally tried to hush it up, not wishing its scattered parts to fall into Soviet hands. But UFO fanatics proclaimed that something very different had happened; that an alien spacecraft had crash-landed, killing its occupant, whose corpse the film purported to show.

'I think it could have been a much better fake,' says one of the *Inquirer*'s writers, Trey Stokes, a Hollywood special effects artist who has created monsters and alien creatures for such films as *The Abyss*, *Batman Returns*, *RoboCop II*,

---

*The Skeptical Enquirer, published by the Committee for the Scientific Investigation of Claims of the Paranormal, 3965 Rensch Road, Amherst, New York 14228–2743

and *The Blob*, who then explains how he would have set about faking it.

The requirements, he says, were straightforward. The film should look like a 1940s-era documentary. The 'alien' should resemble the popular conception of one – almost human, but not quite – and the dead creature should be seen under dissection by actors pretending to be medical investigators who 'discover' non-human internal organs.

The easiest approach is to get a person who in size and shape most resembles the intended alien, and build a plastic 'body cast' around him. Remove the human subject and you have the basic shape. Then, to give it an outlandish appearance, cover it with alginate, a paste-like substance used by dentists to make tooth casts that quickly solidifies into a rubbery semi-solid. Give the alien six fingers and six toes – ten would be much too ordinary. To do this, wires should be inserted in its 'hands' and 'feet' so that these digits stick out. Then redesign the head so that its face has a peculiar staring expression.

Now the cameras roll and the 'investigators' are seen cutting up the body. They are likely to have employed what Mr Stokes calls 'one of the oldest tricks in the book'. One of them takes a scalpel and attaches a small tube to its side that faces away from the camera. As the scalpel moves, the alien 'blood' flows through the tube so that the scalpel leaves a trail of it. The investigators then extract from the stomach suitably treated livers or kidneys obtained from the local butcher.

So much for how a Hollywood pro would have done the job. But the actual filmed performance, says Joseph Bauer, a surgeon from Cleveland, Ohio, showed monumental incompetence. It was clearly managed by 'poorly advised non-professionals'.

The hooded figures around the cadaver appeared to be wearing bee-keepers' masks that would have neither kept in their own microbes nor protected them from alien ones. They slashed and hacked at the alien, in a manner far removed from the careful, scientific way in which ichthyologists were filmed in 1952 dissecting the prehistoric Coelacanth found fully preserved in the Indian Ocean.

'Inexperienced and unskilled hands are seen groping around randomly and unsystematically, without any sign of efforts to recognize or analyse organ structures, relationships or continuity. The bizarre body contents are blindly chopped out and tossed into pans.'

If this alien was genuine, adds Mr Bauer sarcastically, then the way it was shown being treated in the film was 'a documentation of the crime of the century – the brutal butchery, devastation and destruction both of unique evidence and of an unparalleled opportunity to gain some understanding about this deformed creature.'

Both writers are nervously aware of the danger that their comments may teach/provoke some future UFO faker to produce more believable footage.

How We Lost a Race and Won the World

What happened to Neanderthal Man, the race that populated Europe and the Middle East from 100,000 to 40,000 years ago and then vanished? Their total disappearance is one of the profoundest riddles in history; we have now come slightly closer to solving it.

They were not quite like us, this somewhat sinister people whom H.G. Wells, in a famous short story called 'The Grisly Folk'. They were slightly smaller and stockier than our own ancestors of the time, Cro-Magnon Man (a term taken from the rock shelter in southern France where their remains were discovered in 1868.) The Neanderthals – named after a skeleton found in a cave in the German Neander valley in 1856 – were heavy-featured, strong-jawed with prominent brow ridges on a sloping forehead and probably very hairy. In a word, they must have looked brutish. Did our ancestors massacre them, if, as Wells suggests, they were in the habit of carrying off their children, presumably to eat them?

The saga of the Neanderthals has been ably put together by James Shreeve, an expert on early man, in *Discover*. He concludes that both statements are probably incorrect – especially as no mass graves have ever been found of slaughtered Neanderthals – but that there is an even more extraordinary explanation for their disappearance.

First, the background. All living humans are believed to be descended from a single woman (generally known as

'Eve') who lived in Africa some 200,000 years ago (see Explosion of Ancestors, p. 53). She, of course, had her own ancestors, but the entire descent passes through this one female individual. Between 100,000 and 50,000 years ago the descendants of Eve migrated across Europe and Asia. Their travels brought them into direct contact with the Neanderthals. These were modern man's cousins, but descended from a much older branch of the race. (Both, apparently, had a common ancestor in Homo Erectus who lived in Africa between a million and 700,000 years ago.)

What happened when the two remote branches of humanity met? According to the evidence, absolutely nothing. One would expect the two races either to make love or war, and they did neither. Shreeve admits that this is baffling. 'Humans love to mate. The barriers between races, so cruelly evident in other respects, melts away when sex is at

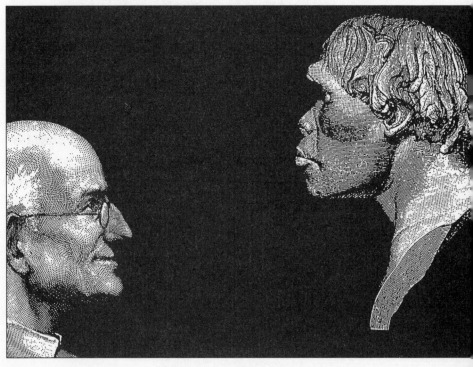

stake.' He points out that Captain Cook's sailors made love without hesitation to Pacific islanders of different skin colour to their own, and that Cortés, conqueror of the Aztecs, for reasons of love or lust rather than politics, married an Aztec princess.

The extraordinary truth appears to be that our Cro-Magnon ancestors co-existed with Neanderthals for 50,000 years and never had sex with them. The reason for this is that they were not the same species, the definition of a species being, in the words of the biologist Ernst Mayr, that they are 'reproductively isolated'. In short, a species is a group that does not mate with anything except itself.

If this definition applies, then the Cro-Magnons were simply not interested in the Neanderthals. They ignored them sexually and socially. They regarded them merely as uninteresting animals.

Judith Masters, of the University of Witwatersrand in Johannesburg, likens this phenomenon to animals – birds or dogs – who respond only to mating calls from members of their own species. 'A female of one species might hear the song of the male of another, but she won't make any response. She doesn't see what all the fuss is about.'

Shreeve suggests that the situation may well have been similar to that of two species of hyrax mammals in East Africa, which look outwardly the same but never mate because the males' penises are of different sizes. They, like the Cro-Magnons and Neanderthals, see each other often but, lacking a common 'fertilization mechanism', take not the slightest notice of each other.

Wealth and success depend on material progress which, in turn, requires a large and mutually cooperating population. The Neanderthals, cut off from the society of their cleverer cousins, can only have gone backwards and perished.

The Deadliest Weapon

When the Mongols besieged a Genoese fortress in the Crimea in 1345, they used the deadliest weapon in history: it killed 75 million people, more than half the human race at the time.

The weapon was the 'trebuchet', the giant siege catapult and the most efficient of all strategic devices until it was superseded by the cannon in the sixteenth century. On this occasion the besiegers fired debris over the town walls which, unknown to them, contained the bubonic plague virus. The disease was then spread to the Mediterranean ports by Genoese sailors.

A fascinating article in *Scientific American* describes the trebuchet's history since its invention in China in the fifth or sixth century BC and the part it played in the expansion of the Islamic and Mongol empires.

The trebuchet was unknown to the Romans, who despised military science, regarding it as an unworthy activity akin to philosophy. Julius Frontinus, Rome's leading military engineer in the second century, wrote: 'I will ignore all ideas for new works and new engines of war, whose invention has reached its limits and for whose improvement I see no further hope.'

Even if his attitude had not been confounded a few centuries later by the superior mounted-archers of the Huns, it would not have survived the trebuchet. Although of little use in a pitched battle on a plain, it was to prove extraordinarily effective in smashing the defences of even the most strongly fortified castles.

At the siege of Acre in 1291, the Mameluke Sultan Al-Ashraf Khalil had as many as 72 trebuchets in action at the same time. One of the *Scientific American* article's authors, Paul Chevedden, a military historian at Salem State College in Massachusetts, wrote: 'Witnesses described his projectiles – great lumps of rock – as "flying hills and mountains".'

According to experiments carried out by Hew Kennedy, formerly an officer in the British Army, trebuchets could hurl a ton of rock 150 metres at speeds greater than 140 kilometres per hour. He has built three replicas of thirteenth-century trebuchets and fired a dead pig, a car and a piano across the English countryside, afterwards selling his machines to the Saudi Government for an exhibition on military history.

The use of trebuchets also had a remarkable effect on the evolution of castles. Walls were made thicker to resist their missiles, and fortifications were strengthened so that

defenders could mount their own trebuchets on top of them. In the thirteenth century, the Citadel in Cairo became the medieval equivalent of a nuclear blast shelter. Strengthened roofs defended the interior against incoming missiles. The Citadel's outer wall was augmented by huge towers supporting trebuchets to prevent the enemy from even bringing his 'artillery' within range.

Not all missiles were intended to kill or destroy. It was common to try to lower the morale of the besieged by firing the severed heads of prisoners at them. There is a horrible scene of this character during the siege of Gondor in Tolkien's novel *The Lord of the Rings*.

The earliest trebuchets were powered by human muscles. The missile was suspended from one end of a swinging beam, and soldiers pulled down the other end so that the missile flew up at an angle of about 45 degrees, to give it the longest trajectory. Later machines had more efficient mechanical counterweights, nicknamed 'testicles' by contemporaries because of their appearance.

Trebuchets unleashed tremendous power, and Chevedden warns those who do not know what they are doing against trying to construct them. Hernan Cortés and his Conquistadors tried to use one when besieging the Aztec city of Tenochtitlan in 1521.

The first stone shot vertically up in the air, only to crash down on the heads of its own builders. 'Would-be replicators should take careful note.'

Explosion of Ancestors

W e can all now boast of a pedigree very much higher – or at least very much more distant. Biologists at Berkeley, California, have concluded that all human beings now alive are descended from one female who lived in Africa some 200,000 years ago.

Many people have found this assertion hard to believe. It might seem at first sight to be arithmetical nonsense. The number of one's ancestors increases as we go back in time. How, then, can we presume to trace our lineage to a single individual who lived nearly 7,000 generations ago?

Consider this argument closely. As everyone has two parents, we can, by allowing about 30 years for a generation, calculate the number of ancestors we had in any given year. We simply divide the number of intervening years by 30, and raise 2 to the power of the answer to that sum. For example, the accession of Queen Victoria in 1837 was about five generations ago. The number of great-great-great grandparents of each of us alive today was thus 2 raised to the fifth power, or 32.

The calculation continues to work reasonably well as we go back in history. At the time of King George III's accession in 1760, each of us had some 256 living ancestors, and back in 1588, when the Spanish Armada was defeated, there were a full 8,192 of them. All well so far, but at a certain point the calculation breaks down.

At the time of the Battle of Agincourt in 1415, each of us ought to have had more than half a million ancestors – more than 10 per cent of the British population – and at the Norman Conquest in 1066 no less than 2,000 million each, which would have vastly exceeded the population of the world at that time!

How could this be? I would suggest that most of these far-off ancestors were the same person. In the early fifteenth century people started almost inevitably to marry their cousins, simply because social strictures and high mortality rates meant that there was no one else to marry.

Even allowing for the terrible ravages of the Black Death, as we look backwards in time our lines of ancestry start to merge. The result is that a full family tree of the human race would be shaped like a tadpole with an exceedingly long tail.

The number of descendants of that remote African ancestor at the tip of the tail who lived 200,000 years ago would at first have grown exceedingly slowly, because of their precarious existence. Hence the long tail.

Then, at the beginning of the Roman Empire, 2,000 years ago, the tail would have greatly thickened. Protected within empires, most people had the prospect of living out their natural lifespans. In later centuries, the multiplication of descendants was as great as that of our own immediate ancestors. Thus the bulging head of the tadpole.

Napoleon as Archaeologist

In campaigns of conquest, the minds of most armies have been on two things – looting and rape. But one exception was Napoleon's occupation of Egypt. As his soldiers rounded a bend in the Nile and saw the temples of Karnak and Luxor amid the ruins of Thebes, a witness tells us, 'the whole army, suddenly and with one accord, stood in amazement and clapped their hands with delight.'

The Egyptian campaign, which began when Napoleon routed the country's despotic Mameluke rulers at the Battle of the Pyramids in 1798, was one of the most important events in the history of science, according to an article in *Scientific American*. The 151 scientists, engineers, doctors and scholars that he brought with him to Egypt – but whom he left behind the following year when he hurried back to Paris to seize power and become First Consul – compiled a mass of information about that country which, for an occupying power, has never been surpassed, says its author, Charles Gillispie, of Princeton University.

Their combined findings, printed between 1809 and 1828 under the title *The Description of Egypt*, were so detailed that they needed a specially designed piece of mahogany furniture to house them (a copy may be seen at the British Library).

They comprised more than 7,000 pages of memoirs, commentaries and maps – and 3 accompanying atlases with records of structures and inscriptions that no longer exist – in 10 folio volumes of plates and 2 atlases containing 837 copper engravings, of which 50 are in colour.

Until Napoleon's arrival, almost nothing was known of Upper Egypt beyond the odd traveller's tale. Its mighty monuments had been abandoned to the sands since the Roman conquest two millennia before. But the French brought Egypt back to life. An example of their work is a magnificent drawing of the south gate of Karnak, drawn as they imagined it originally stood. Resembling a set from Verdi's opera *Aida*, with a victorious Theban king passing through the triumphal arch preceded by his soldiers and followed by his prisoners, it was to inspire Napoleon to build the Arc de Triomphe in Paris.

His scientists were the founders of the science of 'Egyptology'. The language of ancient Egypt used on pharaonic structures was at that time indecipherable. One way to crack a code is to find the same word encrypted in different parts of it. By 1822, Jean-François Champollion had identified the word 'Ptolemy' in the three scripts – hieroglyphic, demotic and Greek – that appear on the Rosetta Stone.

A few decades later, this breakthrough enabled scholars to translate entire texts. The French had meanwhile reluctantly handed over the Stone to the British in 1803, after copying the inscriptions. Ironically, the British had spurred the French cultural mission when Nelson destroyed their fleet in the Battle of the Nile, isolating their army in Egypt.

The French scholars made many other important discoveries. After the army had been tormented during a gruelling desert march by the sight of non-existent lakes, Gaspard Monge identified the true nature of mirages. Jules-Cesar Lelorgne de Savigny disposed of the Biblically inspired myth that Egypt was in constant danger of invasion by venomous flying snakes, symbols of evil, that were kept in check by white ibis birds who preyed on them. The truth, de Savigny declared in his 1805 *Natural and Mythological History* of the Ibis, was that the ibis does not eat flying snakes, which did not exist anyway.

Egypt had long been popularly considered the domain of peculiar animals. An example is Shakespeare's use of the obscure word 'asp' to describe the snake that killed Cleopatra, when he could just as accurately have said 'cobra'.

De Savigny collected more than 1,500 specimens of Egyptian animals and, in doing so, invented the science of 'homology'. This was to be a vital plank in Darwin's theory of evolution, which shows that animals can have organs with the same origin but not necessarily the same function, like the arms of a human and the wings of a bat.

None of this was accidental. Napoleon, uniquely in this campaign, deliberately set out to extend European science to Egypt. He was obsessed by the importance of the East.

The physicist Jean Baptiste Fourier, who accompanied him to Egypt, said: 'He was aware of the influence that the conquest would have on the future relationship between Europe and Asia. His objectives would have been unattainable without the application of science and the technical arts.'

Napoleon's conduct on this occasion was in stark contrast to that of other colonial powers – an extreme example of which was the Belgians' neglect of their African territories which collapsed into ruin when their masters abandoned them.

The Gerontocrats

The rev'rend grey-beards rav'd and storm'd,
That beardless laddies
Should think they better were inform'd
Than their auld daddies.

Robert Burns, *Epistle to Simpson*

C onstant medical improvements are threatening to bring about a crisis that may impoverish us all. People are living to much greater ages. But while their bodies are less affected by time, nothing has yet been invented that will prevent the decay of their minds.

We seem increasingly destined, like China today and the Soviet Union under Brezhnev, to be governed by what Aristotle called 'gerontocracies', the rule of the old and mentally infirm. The statistics are explicit. The number of Europeans aged 65 and over has nearly doubled in the last three decades, from 47 million to 93 million. By 2025, according to the OECD (Organization for Economic Cooperation and Development), a quarter of all Europeans could be above 65, and in Japan, where people live longer than anywhere else (men to 75.6 years and women to 81.4), new records are continually being set. Even in the United States, the average age has risen to a record: 32.3.

Decades of propaganda against the imagined perils of overpopulation have produced a growing demographic disaster. Birth rates have fallen – as the propagandists wanted them to fall – but this fall is combining with better medicine for the old to produce a population increasingly dominated by physically healthy but mentally deficient old people.

The worst prospect is that they will increasingly predominate in governments. Judging from past precedents, this trend could prove catastrophic. Thousands of years before Shelley's warning that 'old men are testy, and will have their way', people were falling into the dangerous habit of submitting themselves to Councils of Elders and similarly named gerontocrats.

Sparta, once the most vigorous and promising civilization of the ancient world, was ruined by its Gerousia, its governing body of 23 members, none of whom was permitted to be younger than 60. The Gerousia enjoyed absolute power, even over their own kings. They could condemn anyone to death without trial, and they boasted of their power to veto all 'crooked' decisions of the people. Thucydides had this to say of Sparta after it had won the Peloponnesian War, only to let itself be destroyed by the corruption and senile petulance of the Gerousia:

> 'Suppose the city of Sparta to be deserted and nothing left but the temples and the ground plan. Distant ages would be very unwilling to believe that its power was at all equal to its fame. Their city has no splendid temples or other edifices. It rather resembles a group of villages and would therefore make a poor show.'

It was shortly before this that the ancient world was besieged by a dynasty of aged tyrants, the Persian kings. The last of these, Xerxes, ordered the sea to be given a thousand lashes as a punishment for drowning his soldiers. 'Treacherous water!' he exclaimed. 'Xerxes the king will cross you, with or without your permission!' – for age and despotism combined find it hard to endure opposition from any source, even an inanimate object.

One is similarly reminded of King Frederick William of Prussia in his dotage, of whom Macaulay says:

'The habit of exercising arbitrary power had made him frightfully savage. His rage constantly vented itself in curses and blows. When His Majesty took a walk, every human being fled before him as if a wild beast had broken loose from a menagerie. If he met a lady in the street, he gave her a kick, and told her to go home and mind her brats. If he saw a clergyman, he admonished the reverend gentleman to betake himself to study and prayer, and he enforced this pious advice with a sound caning.'

The deterioration of the mind in old age may be likened to a computer whose chips are continually failing and not being replaced. At the prime of life, all parts of the brain are interconnected by about 10,000 million neurons, or nerve cells. The electronic pathways of a computer are sequential, which explains both its lightning speed and dumb stupidity. But the brain's equivalents, neurons, being interconnected, give it far more brilliance and versatility although with much slower reasoning power. In old age, as the neurons die, the brain functions with progressively reduced efficiency. Steps in reasoning are omitted because the necessary neurons are no longer alive.

Thus, in the words of the *Encyclopedia Britannica*, old people 'may become self-centred, emotionally unstable, set in their ways, and suspicious of friends and family'. This has nothing to do with disease (although disease or debauchery will aggravate the condition), but results from the natural decay of tissue with time.

The loss of mental vigour can have spectacular consequences. One of the least expected was Napoleon's victory at Austerlitz in 1805, fighting an allied army nearly a third larger than his own. Few historians have come up with the simplest explanation of this brilliant exploit: the average age of Napoleon and his eight subordinate commanders was 39, while their principal opponent, the Russian general Kutusov, was 60.

Many works of creative genius are thus accomplished in early youth. Isaac Newton was only 23 when he discovered the 3 laws of gravitation. The Black Prince won the Battle of Crecy at the age of 16. Edward Gibbon had mastered Greek by the time he was 5, and Mozart wrote his first symphony at the age of 8.

By contrast, Gladstone, aged 84 and in a state of mind which Queen Victoria called 'wild and incomprehensible', mishandled the Irish Question with consequences that linger to this day. The Ayatollah Khomeini reduced his country from prosperity to ruin. Leonid Brezhnev ruled Russia for 6 years after a stroke at the age of 70 which rendered him 'clinically dead'. 'Manipulated by his corrupt entourage,' said a historian, 'he could no longer understand what was going on.'

But there are noble exceptions. It will never be forgotten how Ronald Reagan, at the age of 72, in a few semi-coherent remarks known as the 'Star Wars speech', helped to bring about the collapse of the communist empire.

Gerontocracy is the commonest form of government in history. For tens of thousands of years before there were monarchies and republics, it is believed that our ancestors were invariably governed by the elders of the tribe. They stood as guardians of tradition, and their years commanded prestige and authority – from which it was often falsely concluded that their wisdom could be equally relied on.

The slowness of technological progress in the 100,000 years between the coming of Homo Sapiens and the start of civilization may have been partly caused by gerontocracy. Today, it seems a greater threat even than overpopulation. It can be fought only by opposing foolish measures aimed at reducing birth rates.

Nostradamus was a Journalist – not a Prophet

As the millennium approaches, there will be an ever-increasing number of baseless panics. 'From now on, every time there is an earthquake, a flood or a war, mystical scare-mongers will attribute it to the approach of the Second Coming or some supernatural catastrophe,' said James 'the Amazing' Randi, the conjuror and debunker of mysticism.*

'Let us hope that none of the panic takes the form of mass destruction of property, like the neglecting and burning of crops which in France preceded the first millennium in AD 1000.'

*See his excellent book, *The Mask of Nostradamus* (1995)

The man who was unwittingly most responsible for this hysteria was the sixteenth-century physician, astrologer and gossip Michel de Notredame, more generally known as Nostradamus. He spent much of his life writing down large numbers of 'centuries', or mysterious verses which, it is now claimed, predicted in detail such events as the Great Fire of London, the French Revolution, the rise of Hitler, Watergate, the destruction wreaked by the latest hurricane, and now the imminent end of the world.

But Randi, who has made a major study of Nostradamus, believes his rhymes described events in his own age and were written in semi-code to avoid angering churches and governments. One of them, compiled in 1555, ran:

> *The blood of the innocent will be an error at London,*
> *Burned by thunderbolts, of twenty-three, the six(es),*
> *The senile lady will lose her high position,*
> *Many more of the same sect will be slain.*

Some people have claimed that this was a prediction of the Blitz of 1940, and that the 'senile lady' was St Paul's Cathedral. But in Randi's view it was Nostradamus's righteous horror at the burning of Protestants by Bloody Mary, the only problem being that we don't know what he meant by the 'twenty-three'.

The victims, Randi points out, were offered gunpowder to tie between their legs to shorten their suffering, and which exploded when the flames reached them. This would explain the 'thunderbolts'. They were always executed in groups of six. The 'senile lady' is Queen Mary herself who was reputed to be mad and who, during these executions, wandered naked round her palace, falsely boasting that she bore the child of King Philip II of Spain. Protestants, of whom Nostradamus was secretly one, eagerly hoped for her death.

But this kind of reasoning will make no impression on those to whom prophesying is a profitable trade. Randi has these cynical ground rules for would-be prophets:

• Make lots of predictions, and hope that some will come true. If they do, point to them with pride. Ignore the others. Be very vague and ambiguous. Definite statements can be wrong, but 'possible' items can always be reinterpreted. Use modifiers like these wherever possible: 'I feel that . . .', 'I see a picture of . . .' Use a lot of symbolism. Be metaphorical, using images of animals, names, initials. 'Believers' can fit them to many situations.

• Credit God with your success, and blame yourself for any incorrect interpretations of His divine messages. This way, detractors have to fight God.

• No matter how often you're wrong, plough ahead. The Believers won't notice your mistakes. Predict catastrophes. They are easily remembered and popular.

The 'Nostradamians' – people who exploited the rhymer after his death – are particularly fond of his verses that consist of four lines of ten syllables each, with a strong pause after the fourth syllable of each line, like this one of Randi's:

Nostradamus, in his four-sided hat,
Told his strange tales in a kind of ping-pong.
Hinting at this, making guesses at that,
Too bad for him, but his forecasts were wrong.

'In all,' says Randi, 'Nostradamus was a respectable physician who hated the persecutions and injustices of his day and wrote verses about them that were deliberately obscure to avoid the attention of the Catholic Inquisition in France where he lived. He was ignorant of the world's future and, contrary to popular belief, he had nothing whatever to say about Margaret Thatcher or Donald Duck.'

Who Owns History?

The study of mankind's past is being blotted out by new forms of one of the oldest religious taboos. The belief that the dead should not be disturbed – even after millennia – is prohibiting the study of ancient bones.

By invoking religious antecedents, ethnic and cultural tensions across the world are being given new power. In the United States, Australia and the Middle East, laws are being passed forcing anthropologists and archaeologists to return unearthed bones and artifacts of early man to aborigines and religious authorities.

'It's like saying a biologist can't use a microscope any more or a chemist can't use chemicals,' says Israel Hershkovitz, an anthropologist at Tel Aviv University. 'Bones were our window to the past, and now they've shut that window. It's the death verdict for us.'

An article called 'Who Owns the Past?' in an issue of *Science* described the troubles of Australian scientists at La Trobe University in Victoria. They put together a record of 35,000 continuous years of human habitation in Tasmania, an epoch in which the Pacific was first colonised by migrants from Asia. Tasmanian aborigines, backed by a recent 'heritage' law, demanded that the entire collection be handed over to them. The scientists refused, fearing, on precedent, that the aborigines intended to throw the lot into a lake. The Tasmanian Government promptly revoked the scientists' licence to excavate.

In Israel, where the government depends on the support

of the Orthodox Jewish Party in the Knesset, the Attorney-General forced the Antiquities Authority to hand over its vast and diverse collection of skeletons from the last 5,000 years to the Religious Affairs Ministry, where they are now stored in unmarked boxes.

This figure of 5,000 years at first seemed significant because Orthodox Jews believe that man began about that time. The scientists hoped that they could dig up still older bones with impunity. But a new Bill before the Knesset would give the religious Ministry control over all bones. 'Israel has turned its back on the twentieth century,' says Patricia Smith, of Hebrew University of Jerusalem.

What is being lost is knowledge of prehistory during which global society became what it is. Only a limited amount of such information survives in written form.

We know little, for instance, of the Phoenicians, the great seafaring predecessors of the Romans, or of the Hittites, the martial civilization that defeated the forces of the otherwise all-conquering Pharaoh Rameses II at the Battle of Kadesh in Syria in 1299 BC – a town that has long since vanished.

The Hittites, whose little-known empire lasted nearly a thousand years, are especially interesting because they were responsible for one tremendous technical achievement that transformed the prospects of mankind. They were the first to make their weapons from meteoritic iron, replacing the weaker bronze that was used in the Trojan War and which may explain why the empire lasted so long.

American anthropologists tell a similar tale. When Rob Bonnischsen, of Oregon State University at Corvallis, found some human hairs at a 12,000-year-old site in south-western Montana, he fell foul of the 1990 Native American Graves Protection and Repatriation Act. The hairs were not even from buried bones. They were scattered all over the site. But he was forced to return them unstudied to representatives of Indian tribes.

Knowledge of nearly all events in prehistory is now in jeopardy. It is increasingly difficult to discover how and when people first migrated from Russia to America, from China to Australia, and of the countless races who passed through the Mediterranean and fought on its shores. Everywhere the scientists dig, they are liable to arouse the fear – expressed by ultra-Orthodox Jews – that disturbing graves will 'release vengeful spirits'. American Indians say the dead from disturbed graves 'remain in limbo and cannot enter the spirit world'. But were they not already in the spirit world before their graves were disturbed?

Even discussion of early man is being censored. An Australian television station recently had to withdraw a documentary, 'Out of Time, Out of Place', after an aboriginal group claimed it was offensive.

Volcanoes and Revolutions

C an a volcanic eruption on the other side of the world topple a king and start a reign of terror? According to two French vulcanologists, Roland Rabatin and Philippe Rocher, the answer is yes.

Despite a distance of thousands of kilometres and a time lag of six years, they say the 1783 eruptions of Mount Asama in central Japan, and of Mount Laki in southern Iceland, set off the French revolution which shook the world, produced two decades of war, and led indirectly to two centuries of unrest.

Like the eruption of Mount Pinatubo in the Philippines in 1991, the eruptions blew massive amounts of sulphurous ash into the atmosphere, partly blocking the Sun's radiation and temporarily cooling the climate.

France in 1789 was already in social chaos. Bankrupt because of a long war in America, the government, a mixture of oppression and supine weakness, was threatened by a conspiracy to organize riots financed by an ambitious duke who wanted to seize the crown. But none of this would have produced a revolution had not the country at the same time been faced with famine. The aftermath of the eruptions brought several years of cold wet weather to Europe. Two violent storms in 1788 and 1789 destroyed the harvest in many parts of the country, and the resulting shortage of corn was aggravated by the Finance Minister's refusal to import corn from abroad on the grounds that the state could not afford it.

The result was an explosion of violence which reduced the corn supplies still further. In the words of the historian Nesta Webster:

'When the peasants of France saw wagons laden with wheat winding their way through village streets, voices were not lacking to whisper: "There is corn in plenty, but it is not for you; it is for the Court, the aristocrats, the rich, who will feast in plenty while you go hungry." And forthwith the maddened people would hurl themselves on the sacks of corn and fling them into the nearest river.'

Another volcanic eruption – leading to a massive lowering of temperatures – at Tambora in Indonesia in April, 1815, may have contributed to Napoleon's defeat at Waterloo. This led to a massive lowering of temperatures for several years, in

particular 1816 which was called the 'year without a summer'. Torrential rains marked the outset of the Waterloo campaign, creating deep mud which for many hours prevented Napoleon from moving his guns. (Wellington's guns, deployed earlier, were already well positioned.)

The French Revolution is one of many instances where a change of climate – allied to stupidity – was the final blow to an already precarious civilization.

The Little Ice Age, which started about AD 1400, destroyed the Scandinavian colony in Greenland. But the colonists obstinately refused to change their social system. 'They might have survived if, instead of sticking to their ecclesiastical aristocratic society, they had moved from farming to hunting, like the Eskimos who replaced them,' says Thomas McGovern, of Hunter College, New York.

At about the same period, the great civilization of the Mayas in Yucatan faced ever worsening droughts. Bruce Dahlin, of Howard University, Washington, who has studied its downfall, said: 'Instead of improving their agriculture, their rulers waged endless wars to acquire more arable land. This had the opposite effect to that intended, since recruiting peasants into the armies meant abandoning the land.'

The Bronze Age empire of Mesopotamia also collapsed from drought about 2000 BC. According to Arlene Rosen, of Ben Gurion University in Israel: 'Their fall was more subtly triggered. They successfully endured two fairly short periods of drought. This gave them the false confidence that they could survive the much longer one that destroyed them.'

What lessons can be drawn for the future? A stable civilization will be immune to any but the most catastrophic climatic change. The exceptionally violent eruption of Krakatoa in 1883, for example, caused no social disasters. Only societies which behave stupidly will perish when nature turns foul.

Egypt's White City

One of the most important lost cities of the ancient world is being brought back to life. Some 30 kilometres south-east of Port Said, archaeologists have found the relics of a cosmopolitan city surrounding a huge fortress. It is the remains of Pelusium, an imperial Roman stronghold on the Mediterranean shore of Sinai that for some 1,200 years was the military gateway between Europe and the East.

They are working in frantic haste, since a new canal is about to cover the site, destroying it for ever, just as, in the 1960s, the building of the Aswan Dam and the creation of Lake Nasser flooded the ancient temples of Abu Simbel.

Pelusium, second only in importance to Alexandria as an Eastern city, flourished from before the time of the Ptolemies, some five centuries BC until the eighth century AD, when the Pelusiac branch of the Nile on which it stood finally silted up, and the great city fell into oblivion. This city was the natural gateway to the Orient, a fact that may explain how, in the first millennium BC, it became the earliest known source of the plague.

The prophet Ezekiel called it the 'stronghold of Egypt'. Here Cambyses, king of Persia, invaded Egypt in 525 BC, only to see his army swallowed up by a sandstorm – an experience that turned him from a wise and tolerant ruler into a tyrannical madman.

Alexander the Great passed through it in his victorious pursuit of Darius, another Persian king. So did Augustus on

his way to defeat Cleopatra and Mark Antony at the Battle of Actium. So also, according to legend, did the Holy Family, fleeing from Palestine on donkeys with Herod's soldiers in close pursuit. Their flight became a cornerstone of the faith of the Egyptian Copts, who built churches to mark important stages of their journey.

Three centuries later, in a mood of ruthless anger, the emperor Diocletian marched through it to suppress a rebellion that had convulsed Alexandria for eight months. Having pacified that city by the indiscriminate slaughter of thousands, he collected all ancient books there and in Pelusium that explained how to mint gold and silver coins. These, says a contemporary, 'he committed without pity to the flames, lest the opulence of the Egyptians should again inspire them with confidence to rebel against the empire'.

Pelusium remained a place of mystery after its fall until the Egyptians, having made peace with Israel, decided to irrigate the Sinai Desert with a new canal called Salaam ('Peace'). Only now has it started to yield important remains. Excavators are amazed by the size and grandeur of the ruin. 'It is changing everything we thought we knew,' said their leader, Mohammed Abdel Maksoud. 'In one moment we've altered the face of the desert.'

They have found that the central town was defended by 12 towers and walls, enclosing a fortress 20 times bigger than a modern football field. Its mud-brick walls are unique in Egyptian ruins, since they are coloured white. 'Perhaps they mixed chalk with mud,' said Maksoud. 'We don't know, because we've never seen anything like this.'

The place is a treasure chest of relics. It abounds with amphora, human bones, fallen columns, and coins stamped with the faces of many an ancient ruler. Diggers unearthed a worn limestone statue of a lion, his front paws crossed, and later, a coloured erotic sculpture of a smiling naked male bather that once adorned a Roman bath.

The city had all the imperial trappings, with a race-course, public baths, and an amphitheatre complete with tiers of red-brick seats and a sea-facing circular stage of mosaic-shaped limestone bricks.

'They called this place the island of Pelusium, but we didn't know why until we started digging,' said Maksoud. 'But we now see that it would have looked like an island. To the south was a branch of the Nile, to the north the Mediterranean, and in the middle the city.'

All now that remains to be found, before Pelusium vanishes, is the Church of the Holy Family, the memorial that must have been built by the Copts to mark the flight of Jesus.

Part Two

THE WAY
WE LIVE NOW

The Locksmith's Daughter

Some of the millions of people who leave their homes empty during holidays worry about the 'locksmith's daughter'.

This is a slang name either for the legitimate key to a lock, or a way for a thief to bypass it. For, like a chain, a lock is only as strong as its weakest link.

No home owner wants to be in the position of the pompous banker in the Sherlock Holmes story 'The Red-Headed League' who boasts of the strength of the front doors to his vaults, only to find that a burglar has tunnelled his way through the back wall.

Some older mechanical locks had peculiarly vicious habits. When attacked they would defend themselves. Instead of merely making a noise like a burglar alarm, they were designed to injure intruders. They resembled the deadly serpents or other monsters who guarded hidden treasures in classical myths – or the amazing array of lethal traps that routinely confront Indiana Jones.

One such lock was the Pierce, invented in 1845, which responded to any attempts to pick it. It had a spring-driven steel barb hidden beneath the key hole. If anyone tampered with the lock, the barb would spring out, driving itself deep into the intruder's hand.

According to an article in *Focus* magazine, locks are becoming more and more electronic. They will open, not to a metal key, but to the punching in of a secret password. The art of making secure locks is, in fact, becoming increasingly

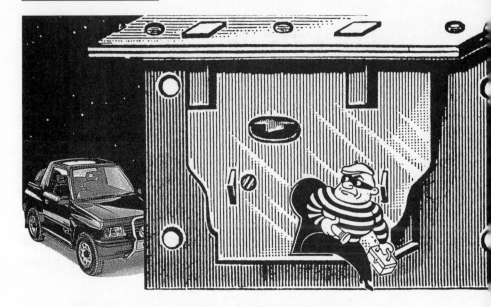

tied to that of making strong computerized ciphers, for the skills have much in common.

A famous puzzle that applies to both is that of the 'Locked Strongbox'. A secret agent called Harry wishes to send a locked box to a confederate named Seamus whom he has never met or communicated with, and which only Seamus can open.

It sounds impossible, but it can be done. Harry locks the box with a padlock and sends it to Seamus. Seamus, without attempting to open it, relocks the box with his own padlock and sends it back to Harry. Harry then removes his padlock and sends the box to Seamus a second time. Seamus can then remove his padlock and open the box.

The ingenious mathematics of this procedure is at the root of 'public key' ciphers in which complete strangers can communicate over the Internet without fear of eavesdroppers. Governments are increasingly terrified at the prospect, fearing that they will be unable to spy on criminals. (Until recently it was illegal in France to send encrypted material by electronic mail.) An American encryption software writer was barred from exporting his system by the State Department who told him that it was a 'munition'. To sell it abroad he would need an arms dealer's licence.

Mechanical locks, as opposed to electronic ones, still have a strong psychological appeal. People like to hear them 'clunk' when they are shut. Smart cards being swiped through an electronic reader control device are distrusted – particularly when, with a soldering iron, a thief can in many cases read what is imprinted on a stolen card. One result of this is that Chubb's new super-secure Electro smart-card device, with its key of 43 numerical digits, makes a satisfying door-clanging noise when it is operated.

The greatest danger in security is the presence of the unsuspected locksmith's daughter. Leave the window open and the strongest door is to no avail. Gordius, king of Phrygia, thought his kingdom safe when he tied a knot of unrivalled complexity and boasted that only the man who knew how to undo it would reign over the East. Alexander the Great 'undid it' with a single slash of his sword.

Belay The Antarctic Tourist!

When A Chinese ship arrived in Antarctica, its crew went ashore and began playing football – using a live penguin as the ball. 'It's the sort of behaviour one expects from uneducated people,' said a British scientist, 'and it illustrates the problems that are going to arise with growing numbers of Antarctic tourists.'

With 7,000 tourists now visiting Antarctica each summer season (September–December), most of them in large cruise liners at a minimum cost of about £3,700 per head, tour operators face increasing hostility from environmentalists, who fear the eventual ruin of the continent.

At a meeting in Madrid of the 26 Antarctic Treaty nations (where America infuriated environmentalists by refusing to accept an indefinite mining ban), plans were postponed to require all tourist ships to obtain 'environmental impact certificates' before they set out, and to prohibit any further construction of Antarctic airstrips.

'The larger tourist ships are not even ice-strengthened,' said Bruce Manheim, of the Washington-based Environmental Defence Fund. 'We don't want another accident like the oil spill in 1989 from the Argentine supply ship *Bahaia Paraiso* which was carrying 81 passengers, and we still don't have regulations to prevent similar catastrophes.'

Scientists take a more relaxed line, tending to welcome tourists so long as they do not arrive unexpectedly, interrupting scientific experiments. There is growing ill-feeling between scientists and diplomats on the one side, and environmentalists on the other. The latter believe the former are blocking their plans to ban commercial mining. One of them called the 3,000 Antarctic scientists 'hired henchmen based on exploitation', while to a scientist the environmentalists were 'elitists kicking up a fuss as a pretext to raise funds'.

'On the whole the tourists behave very well,' said Bernard Stonehouse of the Scott Polar Research Institute in Cambridge, who, in 1995 travelled on the cruise ship *Society Explorer* with a dual role: ostensibly he was a lecturer, but he was also there to observe how the tourists behaved when ashore.

'Their worst habit is interfering with the animals. Photographers are particularly prone to this. They are apt to break into colonies of sleeping seals or brooding penguins. The frightened penguins then abandon their eggs, which are never hatched.'

But tourists – usually called 'expedition members' and their tours called 'projects' – were praised by Stonehouse for doing more to keep Antarctica clean than groups like Greenpeace have ever done.

'In the Sixties, when they first started coming to the large American base at McMurdo Sound, they found piles of refuse which the scientists had dumped there. Saying: "I didn't travel thousands of miles to see this rubbish," they returned to Washington and lobbied their Senators and Congressmen to impose strict clean-up regulations.'

Scientists are especially bitter at the environmentalist campaign against airstrips, which enable people to reach Antarctica in about six hours from Australia, New Zealand, Chile or the Falklands, instead of going by sea, which can take days. 'Airstrips can save lives in a medical emergency,' said Stonehouse, recalling Greenpeace efforts to stop construction of an airstrip at the French Dumont d'Urville base by erecting huts in the path of the bulldozers; and the verbal campaign against the airstrip at the British base at Rothera, for which the British Antarctic Survey has been accused of 'paving the way for destruction' by allowing in mineral prospectors.

But the threat of destructive mineral prospecting and talk of 'ecological fragility' is a myth, said Richard Laws, former director of the Survey. The continent is just too vast to be imperilled by human activities, he argues.

'With an area of 14 million square kilometres, a tenth of the land surface of the Earth, there will not be any strong pressures for commercial mineral-related activities there for a long time.' What he called 'vociferous, well-financed environmentalist groups' were to be blamed for their misinformation.

'The polluting "footprint" of a scientific station is on average less than a square mile. On a map these stations, instead of being a number of large black dots, would be microscopic. There are about 50 manned scientific stations and therefore some 100 square kilometres may be 'significantly' affected, while 99.999 per cent remains virtually unaffected by human activity.

'One idea, much touted by environmentalists, is to turn Antarctica into a "world park". This is unacceptable. It would mean not only severe restrictions on science and tourism, but also gigantic expenditure on policing caused by an expensive, inefficient bureaucracy.'

Antarctica was described by Captain Cook in 1774 as 'lands doomed by nature to perpetual frigidness, never to feel the warmth of the Sun's rays, whose horrible and savage aspect I have not words to describe.' Today the ice-cap continues to attract 'expedition members' who find it distinctly more beautiful and spectacular than he did.

Fatal Doses

T he book, *Dead not Buried*, about Herbert Armstrong, the solicitor hanged in 1922 for murdering his wife with arsenic, is a reminder that poison has through the ages been the classic means of murder.*

'Deadly substances used to be easy to obtain, and the resulting deaths could be made to look natural or accidental,' said John Nicholson, formerly of the Laboratory of the Government Chemist.

One infamous poisoner who took full advantage of this maxim was Professor Yuri Ovchinnikov, vice president of the Academy of Sciences of the former Soviet Union, who died in 1988 after a 'long and grave illness' that might well have been caused by his researches.

Ovchinnikov, suspected of helping to supply some of Saddam Hussein's nerve gas, specialized in creating microbial and other poisons from the venom of snakes, scorpions, wasps, puffer fish and fungoids. During his lifetime, an émigré Soviet biologist called him 'one of the most dangerous men on Earth'.

He planned a genetically engineered bacterial weapon that could have killed millions of people. It would be a poison without cure or antidote that would be equipped with a 'pili', or tentacles, enabling it to stick to the walls of the human intestine. A few days after a vial containing it had been dropped into an enemy city's water-supply, millions

---

Dead not Buried, by Martin Beales (1995)

would perish. Ovchinnikov was also looking for a way to immunize his own nationals against it.

Poison dates back beyond the dawn of writing to when magician-priests first began to explore the toxicity of plants. The Romans, as television viewers of *I, Claudius* know from the technical discussion between Livia and the poisoner Martina, were skilled and enthusiastic in its use. Their enemy, King Mithridates of Pontus, was so frightened of being poisoned that he built himself a fabulous antidote that comprised all the known antidotes to poison mixed up into a single substance. With this in his body, he boasted that he was immune to at least 46 different poisons. But no one ever found out if this was true, since he was killed with a sword.

It is hard to believe that he would have been immune to some of the poisons created or discovered in the twentieth century. Cyanide kills quickly, but chemists have created the compound 2, 3, 7, 8-tetrachlorodibenzo-p-dioxin, or TCDD, the most deadly of the 75 known dioxins, which is 150,000 times more deadly than cyanide. Neither could Mithridates

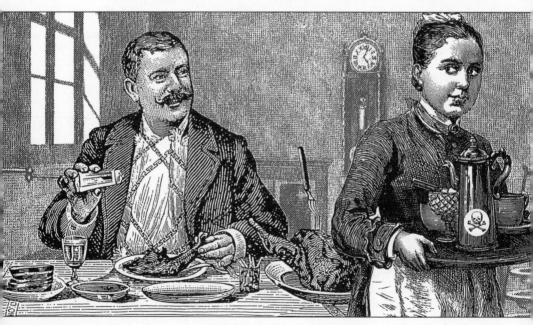

nor anyone else have survived if they inhaled more than a third of a millionth of a gram of the nerve gas ethyl S-2-diisoprovy laminoethylmethyl phosphonothiolate, or VX, developed at Porton Down in 1952, which Alistair MacLean is believed to have used in his novel *The Satan Bug*.

Biological toxins are particularly deadly. Some Indian tribes in Colombia are fond of gathering 'poison arrow frogs' from the rain forests. These secrete a venom so deadly that when arrows dipped in it are used in war, the contents of a single frog can kill 50 men.

'Octopussy', from the James Bond film of that name, is no myth. It is a beautiful, 12-centimetre-wide animal, found in Australian waters, that the *Guinness Book of Records* calls 'blue-ringed and terror-ringed'. A bite from it kills in minutes – just as quickly as the Australian box jellyfish, which releases a cardiotoxic venom when touched by a swimmer.

One of the strongest natural poisons is found only in Britain. It is from the yellowish-olive death cap fungus, *Amanita phalloides*, the world's most poisonous fungus and responsible for 90 per cent of all fatal poisonings caused by fungi. It was used in 1534 to kill Pope Clement VII, a member of the murderous Medici clan, whose poisoning habits can be seen in the 1995 film *La Reine Margot*.

Poisoners appear to enjoy their work. Ovchinnikov, for one, was happy to discuss it. Asked whether his knowledge might be better used for curing diseases than causing them, he replied blandly: 'Not at all. If I bring vaccines to the Central Committee, nobody will pay attention. But if I bring a virus – oh, then this will be recognized by all as a great victory.'

Firkins, Kilderkins and Hogsheads

While many believe that replacing imperial measurements with metric units can be a cultural disaster, others hold the view that an enormous boost to trade awaits us – if only we could bring ourselves to abandon old prejudices.

An eloquent plea to this effect, and a protest against the 'medieval conservatives' who oppose it, is given in *Interdisciplinary Science Reviews* by its editor Anthony Michaelis. Britain and the United States, he points out, still remain obstinate in rejecting metric units to their 'great disadvantage in global markets'.

Just over 200 years ago, he points out, we could have joined the French in establishing the metric system at a cost of a few thousand pounds in modern money. But today it would cost hundreds of millions – even though we would profit hugely in the long term by doing so.

We are indulging in the same obstinacy that for many centuries prevented us from adopting the arithmetical system of writing numbers as numerals and decimal points. This was an invention, not of Arabs as is commonly supposed, but of a brilliant Indian from the province of Gujarat who first proposed it in AD 595, and who has been called the most famous son of India after Buddha.

Without decimals, which took about a millennium to filter through to the Western world – it took that long for us to exploit the fact that we each have ten fingers – modern scientific discoveries would be extremely difficult either to make or describe.

It was not only the numbers but the symbols defining them whose introduction in the West was so long delayed. Right up until the sixteenth century, mathematicians all had their own symbols for an 'equals' sign, which must have made it hard for them to understand each other. At length in 1557, Robert Recorde included in a textbook on algebra this trenchant passage: 'To avoid the tedious repetition of these words is equal to, I will set as I do often in work use a pair of parallels, thus: because no two things can be more equal.' This became contracted in due course to the now-familiar sign: =.

And how, without decimals, could one write about things that were either extremely large or extremely small? Yet the metric system just does that, in language that is almost poetic. Without it, we would even be unable to describe some of the dimensions of the cosmos. The Sun, for example, weighs 2×10^{27} tons, an expression that means 2 followed by 27 noughts. There is just no way to make such a statement without using metric arithmetic. Powers of 10 give us a whole range of invaluable measurements.

The movement towards metrication started in earnest in the late eighteenth century when there were so many units that it is hard to understand how trade could have been conducted. A guidebook of the time reported that in England the following units were used to measure quantities of liquid: gallon, firkin, kilderkin, rundlet, barrel, tierce, hogshead, punchion, pipe and tun. The use of these terms was almost indiscriminate: it depended on where you were buying your goods. The units themselves varied enormously. In 1752, a weight of 100 pounds in Amsterdam was found to equal 105 pounds in Antwerp, 98 in Basel, 111 in Berne, 105 in Brussels, 97 in Dublin, 143 in Florence, 109 in London,

114 in Madrid, 168 in Milan, and 81 in Stockholm. But in Venice, it nearly doubled, to 182 pounds.

When the great chemist Antoine Lavoisier did his historic experiment in 1781 showing that water was not an element but was made up of hydrogen and oxygen, he created a sensation by quantifying one of his measurements with a decimal, writing: '13,6 grains'. (He used a comma, rather than a full stop, or point, a tradition that continues in France to this day.)

This was the crucial moment, indeed the turning point: people realized that no great advances would be made in knowledge or trade without units that all would recognize and on which there were no local variations.

Accordingly in 1790, the French Royal Academy determined that a standard metre was to equal 'one ten-millionth part of the meridian quadrant of the Earth'. And during Napoleon's conquests the metric system spread through Europe – perhaps because people were reluctant to disobey Napoleon.

But there is still resistance to it today. NASA operates its shuttles and is building the space station in feet per second and pounds per square inch. In Britain, the Department of Trade and Industry last considered the matter in 1991, and the Navy uses 30-millimetre, 4½-inch guns and the nautical mile side by side.

And there is a growing cultural divide between the two systems. One scientist said: 'When I see the headline: "80 in the shade – phew what a scorcher!" I find it totally unintelligible.'

Those Juggling Fiends

They brought one Pinch, a hungry lean-faced villain,
A mere anatomy, a mountebank,
A threadbare juggler, and a fortune-teller,
A needy, hollow-eyed, sharp-looking wretch,
A living-dead man.

The Comedy of Errors

A soldier weighing 67 kilos hurrying to the aid of his comrades in the midst of a battle, carries three half-kilo cannon balls across a bridge that will only bear 68 kilos. How does he get the ammunition across the bridge?

The usual answer to this ancient riddle is that he juggles the balls, so that one of them is always in the air. The art – and science – of juggling is now receiving widespread attention as people increasingly use it to study brain and body co-ordination, mathematics and its application to future industrial and domestic robots.

Its fascination has become so widespread that there is even an International Jugglers' Association and a magazine selling 3,000 copies called *Jugglers' World*.

Skills are improving. The eighteenth-century juggler Enrico Rastelli achieved what was then considered almost miraculous: keeping 10 balls in the air at a time. But today the record for the number of objects juggled (where each is thrown and caught at least once) is 11 balls, 12 rings or 8 clubs.

Robots are now being taught to juggle, and not surprisingly they can do so much better than humans. Arthur Lewbel, of Brandeis University in the US, co-author of an article on juggling in the *Scientific American* writes: 'Even if its pattern breaks down, instead of dropping the balls, the robot can recover and resume with astonishing swiftness.'

Juggling, as Lewbel points out, is difficult for the following reasons: each ball (or other object) must be thrown sufficiently high to allow the juggler time to deal with the others. The time that a ball spends in flight is proportional to the square root of the height of the throw. This means that the need for height and strength increases rapidly with the number of objects thrown.

A great hope is that a robot that has been taught to juggle will have the dexterity to perform tasks that people find tiresome. Clearing a table after a meal, for example, requires enormous delicacy and precision, far removed from the brute force of most robots, which do only such things as driving rivets into car bodies. Plates, glasses and cutlery must be removed and placed in the dishwasher without being broken. After washing, they must be removed from the machine and placed in their correct positions in cupboards. It was believed until recently that a century might elapse before robots could do such things; the new forecast is that experimental domestic robots capable of such feats may appear within a few years.

Jugglers have tended to have a bad press. Being so clever, they were generally viewed as manipulative and disreputable. Theologians were fond of accusing their opponents of 'juggling with the scriptures', so as to 'draw them into carnal and fleshly purpose'. Macbeth called the witches who tantalized him 'juggling fiends', and Batman has an especially evil enemy called the Juggler.

The art of juggling goes back thousands of years. There is even a depiction of women jugglers – some riding on others' shoulders – on the tomb of an unknown Egyptian prince carved in the second millennium BC. Even animals have been taught to juggle. In Russian circuses, a bear sometimes lies on a cradle juggling a flaming torch with its hind legs.

But the popular answer to the riddle of the soldier and the cannon balls is false. Catching a falling ball would exert a force that would break the bridge.

10 GOTO 10*

A computer program called 'Literary Expert' announces that Dickens's novel *A Tale of Two Cities* cannot be appreciated by anyone aged less than 43.

British tax revenues will fall significantly short in 1997 because the new computer software designed for self-assessment is riddled with bugs.

A cancer-therapy machine goes berserk in several American and Canadian hospitals, shooting fatal overdoses of radiation into at least six patients.

These are examples of one of a growing crisis, bugs in computer software, errors in the innumerable lines of 'source code' which tell a computer what to do. They are always there accidentally, because the programmer has made mistakes, and must not be confused with malicious computer 'viruses', which are deliberately designed to make computers inoperable.

The problem is worsening because, as an article in the American science magazine *Discover* points out, programs are being ever bigger – as the memory storage capacity of computers themselves becomes ever greater – and software typically consists of tens, or hundreds of thousands of lines of source code.

The bugs in such vast programs cannot all be found by printing out the source code and scanning it by eye. The

---

*The command in IBM Basic 10 GOTO 10 is a classic bug that creates a 'perpetual loop', causing the screen to freeze and leaving the user bewildered and helpless unless he can track the error down and correct it.

program has to be exhaustively tested, which means discovering how it will behave in all conceivable circumstances. But there will always be circumstances that the programmer has not thought of, and there the bugs will lurk. In the words of Peter Newmann, a computer expert at SRI International in Menlo Park, California: 'Guaranteed system behaviour is impossible to achieve.'

Obvious errors are easily spotted. If part of the program that asks the user for information contains the word IMPUT instead of INPUT, the program will pronounce: 'syntax error', and wait for it to be corrected. But more subtle errors will be less easily found. Some have had amusing consequences, and some tragic:

• A 'Political Analyst' program of the seventies, designed as an experiment to make computers behave 'intelligently', announced that the Communist Chinese must have built the Berlin Wall. It concluded this because China, under Mao's dictatorship, appeared to be the most militant Communist power. The programmer had failed to tell the program that the Chinese did not have access to Berlin.

• A journalist writing an article about the climate on his word processor included the phrase 'furious gales'. On putting the article through the program's grammar checker, he was told: 'This is a disrespectful way to refer to women.'(The programmer had allowed 'gales' to be construed as 'gals'.)

• A popular book on computing contained the source code for what was claimed to be a powerful chess-playing program. I copied it out carefully, checking each line. But when executed, it merely said: 'Thank you for playing. Another game (Y/N).'

• In 1991, an 'improvement' was introduced to the program that runs the American telephone system. 'It was only a minor change,' said Newmann, 'so they assumed they could release it without testing it.' But it disrupted phones in Pittsburgh, Los Angeles, San Francisco and Washington, and it took weeks to find the bugs.

• During the Gulf War, a seemingly tiny error in the radar and tracking system of the Patriot missile changed its timing by one third of a second. On 25 February 1991, it missed an incoming Scud missile which killed 29 American soldiers in a Saudi Arabian barracks.

Since even a comparatively simple program can be more complicated than a motor car, commercial programs are usually not written by individuals but by teams. Each member writes his own 'module', and at the end they are all stuck together to make one entity.

The danger comes when one team-member has tried to be too clever or not imaginative enough, and the modules do not fit properly. Bugs can often be eliminated by introducing a new 'rule' to the existing program that says: 'If such-and-such is the case, then do so-and-so.' The Literary Analyst would not have made its mistake about Dickens if the programmer had remembered to tell it that people reach intellectual maturity at the age of 18.

Tentacles from the Sea

P eople who take Mediterranean holidays cannot always plunge safely into the cool sea. For they may be in peril from that most dangerous and beautiful marine object, the ubiquitous jellyfish.

From the English coasts to the beaches of Australia, hundreds of swimmers and divers are killed or severely injured by jellyfish every year. Whether it is due to some peculiarity of wind and current, or the reopening of the Suez Canal (theories abound, but nobody really knows the reason), Mediterranean waters seem more infested than ever. Glittering Aegean bays that yesterday were free of them can turn today into menageries of sinister floating shapes. The deadliest species of all is *Chironex fleckeri*, the so-called box jelly, also known as the sea wasp. It can kill in seconds.

On the northern coast of Australia, beach guards have adopted an extraordinary means of protecting themselves. They wear two pairs of women's pantyhose, one for the legs and the other worn upside down for the torso, with a hole cut in the crotch for the head. Experts assure us that the box jellies are to be found only between the Tropic of Capricorn and the Equator, that is to say in the southern seas. But experts are often wrong, particularly in the mysteries of marine biology.

These creatures might, for all we know, be migrating northwards. A box jelly is similar in appearance to many other species of jellyfish. It has a small bell-shaped body, about 25 centimetres across and, less visibly, some sixty

18-metre tentacles trailing beneath them. The tentacles are covered with millions of 'nematocysts', derived from the Greek word *nema*, meaning thread. They contain the stings. A nematocyst fires out toxins like a tiny gun with such force that it can penetrate a glove, although not, apparently, pantyhose.

A single jellyfish can have several types of nematocyst, each with a different poison. Some stop the heart of an adult by interfering with the passage of calcium through the myocardial membrane. Another disrupts the circulatory system by destroying red blood cells. A third can penetrate the brain and stop the victim from breathing.

More commonly, multiple stings can produce hideous welts all over the body, accompanied by headache, nausea and fever. These welts, found on two dead men formed the mystery of the Sherlock Holmes story 'The Lion's Mane'. They seemed to have been flogged to death: but Sir Arthur Conan Doyle had made a rare mistake, for the stings of that huge lion's mane jellyfish with its 600-metre tentacles are usually too mild to be dangerous.

Only a few dozen of the approximately 500 known species of jellyfish are dangerous to humans. And people are affected in different ways. Some take no ill effect; others, with allergies, are laid low.

Why has nature, in the form of evolution by natural selection, filled the seas with such horrible creatures? The answer, according to scientists, is that the jellyfish need their stings for protection and to prey on fish, and it is just bad luck that humans are poisoned by their venom.

A jellyfish has nothing that we could call a brain. A shark is a genius by comparison. Like the Venus's fly-trap plant, a jellyfish attacks by instinct rather than by calculation. Yet instinctive behaviour can be extraordinarily complex. There is one species of jellyfish known as *Velella velella* which, instead of moving with the current, actually sails. It sticks a fin out of the water which the wind propels. It is not a particularly 'good' sailor, for it 'tacks' up to 60 degrees from the wind direction. And stranger still, there appear to be two species of *velella*, those that sail on the starboard tack and those that sail on the port.

Do these species intermingle? Nobody knows. Big jellyfish like the Portuguese man-of-war and the box jelly are formidable enough, but who knows what monstrous jelly-cousins, with awful destructive powers, may exist at the bottom of the deepest oceans, tens of thousands of metres down, where animals grow to gigantic sizes? Those who explore the depths of the seas in manned submersibles may soon be making some unpleasant discoveries.

Rushing for Emeralds

An 'emerald rush' may follow reports that explain for the first time the ideal natural conditions for the production of these most lustrous green gems.

Ever since the Spanish conquistadors looted the silver, diamond and emerald mines of South America in the sixteenth century, it has been known that emeralds with the finest inner lustre are found only in Colombia, the world's leading emerald

producer, where – unlike diamonds or other precious gems – they are formed differently from anywhere else.

The reports have set off a search for new emerald mines whose gem quality may match that of Colombia, and also put an end to the dreams of alchemists through the ages who have tried to manufacture them.

Emeralds are much rarer than diamonds and, ounce for ounce, are thousands of times more valuable than gold. In one recent year alone, Colombian exports of emeralds produced revenues of £41 million. This may explain why, in Colombia, emeralds can fetch 50 times more money than cocaine, and dealing in them can be an extremely violent business. An estimated 4,000 people were killed in a five-year 'green war' that ended in 1992.

It was once believed that producing the best emeralds was a matter of alchemical skill. Anthony Fallick, of the Scottish Universities Research and Reactor Centre in Glasgow, writing in *Nature*, has unearthed this splendid passage from an anonymous tract called the Papyrus *Graecus Holmiensis*, written in Egypt about AD 400:

'For the preparation of emerald: mix together in a small jar ½ drachma of copper green (verdigris), ½ drachma of Armenian blue (chrysocolla), ½ cup of the urine of an uncorrupted youth and ⅔ the fluid of a steer's gall. Put into this the stones, about 24 pieces weighing about ½ obolus [a gold or silver coin] each. Put the lid on the jar, seal the lid all around with clay, and heat for six hours over a gentle fire made of olive-wood. You will find they have become emeralds.'

But Colombian geology creates emeralds much more efficiently than the lavatorial leavings of uncorrupted youths. Most important is the presence of sulphur. At Muzo, in bandit-infested country some 60 miles from Bogotá and

Colombia's most famous emerald mine, geologists discovered a region where millions of years ago sulphates dissolved in salty hot water. As Fallick points out: 'When the sulphur reacts with organic matter to release chromium, vanadium and beryllium, the essential ingredients of the best quality emeralds, it removes from them the iron impurities which elsewhere quench their natural luminescence.'

Emerald lovers will be enthusiastic for many reasons. Prized for their beauty at least since 1650 BC when emeralds were mined in Upper Egypt, they have long been reputed in legend as cures for bad eyesight and epilepsy, an aid for women in childbirth, and for driving away evil spirits and blinding snakes and dragons.

Two Sherlock Holmes stories, 'The Beryl Coronet' and 'The Six Napoleons', are about stolen emeralds while the anonymous 1889 poem 'Birth-stones' contains this sentimental verse:

> *Who first beholds the light of day*
> *In Spring's sweet flowery month of May*
> *And wears an emerald all her life,*
> *Shall be a loved and happy wife.*

One of the world's largest emeralds, a 430-carat carved gem the size of a small apple, was recently sold to an anonymous buyer at Bonhams in London for £231,000. Although this was the largest single emerald ever sold at an auction, it barely compared in size with an 86,136-carat gem found in Brazil in 1974, valued at £718,000.

The 430-carat emerald had a typical history. Originating in Colombia, it was carved for a high official at the Mogul court in India in about 1695. Indian rulers wore emeralds as often as possible in the mystical belief that displaying them in public would preserve their wealth.

The search for emerald mines to match the quality of Colombia has thrown up geologically favourable areas in Brazil, Australia, Pakistan, India and Afghanistan. Of these, Afghanistan, where the Mujahideen used emeralds to finance their war against the Soviet Union, may be a hazardous place to look.

Nature is by far the best producer of emeralds. It will probably never be safe to make them at home in basements. 'The element beryllium is extremely dangerous to handle and its dust and fumes can cause fatal illness,' said Terri Ottaway, of the Royal Ontario Museum in Toronto.

Spitting Images and Fatal Errors

When aberdeen University zoologist Roger Thorpe and his staff enter their laboratory they wear surgical masks and goggles and carry grappling sticks. It is the home of 12 deadly snakes, including several spitting cobras whose venom can cause blindness, serious injury or even death.

'Unlike the cunning rock python Kaa in Kipling's *Jungle Book*, snakes are extremely stupid,' says Thorpe. 'They do not recognize individual people, and spitting cobras in particular are very bad tempered. They can cover you with venom from a range of two metres.'

With the aid of computerized databases, he and his colleague Wolfgang Wuster are making remarkable discoveries about venomous snakes, leading to important changes in the treatment of people who suffer snakebite.

'There are about 400 species of deadly snakes,' says Thorpe, 'and about 2,500 non-deadly ones. About 40,000 people are killed by the deadly variety every year, and more than 10 times that number suffer lasting injuries, ranging from dead skin-tissue to gangrene. The problem, all too often, is that victims are given the wrong antidote, because it was designed to counter the venom of a different snake.

'Detailed studies, never carried out until now, have shown us that many of these animals belong to completely different species, with common ancestors who lived millions of years ago. The result of these evolutionary divergences is that they have different venoms which require different antidotes.'

Asiatic cobras, found from semi-desert Central Asia to tropical Indonesia, look the same at a cursory glance and are lumped together as a single species known as *Naja naja*. But that name ought to belong solely to the Indian spectacled cobra, found in India, Sri Lanka, Pakistan, Nepal and Bangladesh.

The misunderstanding among experts outside the sub-continent is 'little short of stunning', says Wuster. Because the difference was not appreciated, cobra victims elsewhere in Asia have been treated with the antidote for *Naja naja*, often with fatal results. Thorpe and his team have now found from the evidence of their snakes' scales, colour patterns and position of internal organs that there are at least ten species of Asiatic cobra.

Unfortunately the attitudes of the snake scientists have differed as markedly as the snakes themselves. Biologists who study snakes for general scientific reasons, and those like Thorpe and Wuster who try to classify them into species with an eye to developing correct antidotes, seem to live in different parallel universes. 'They hold us in disdain,' Wuster complains. 'We are often regarded as rather pompous people sitting in museum back rooms, counting scales all day and confusing everyone by changing scientific names for no good reason.'

One case of bad decision-making resulting from this attitude led to considerable loss of life among rice farmers living in a densely populated region of Malaysia and Thailand. Also living there are two species of snake of almost identical appearance, the monocellate cobra and the equatorial spitting cobra.

Despite obvious differences in size, colour patterns and behaviour, the distinction between the two species was largely unreported in scientific literature. Authorities added to the confusion. Thailand manufactured and distributed an antidote against the venom of the first snake, while the Malaysian antidote was effective only against that of the second. Not surprisingly, people bitten by the one and treated for a bite by the other died or became seriously ill.

Nobody is proposing the extermination of venomous snakes, since non-venomous kinds would inevitably be destroyed along with them, and without snakes the rat population would explode, with consequent destruction of crops. 'Only a snake is narrow enough to crawl into a rat burrow and eat their litter,' says Thorpe.

Instead, there is a growing belief that dangerous animals must be protected to preserve genetic diversity. 'To do both this and protect human life at the same time,' says Wuster, 'the best approach is to ask the simple but fundamental question: "What's what?" '

Nonsense on the Screen

W hy did the science fiction film *Terminator II, Judgement Day* pack cinemas throughout the country when it appeared in 1991?

It was not just that its estimated budget of $100 million made it the most expensive film ever made, nor because of its tremendous special effects; but rather because audiences found the exciting story plausible and therefore suspected it might be good science. While some of its scenes are over the top, its general scientific quality is an extraordinary improvement on the kind of SF films that were being made in earlier decades.

In those days producers knew practically nothing about science; they made no effort to learn any, and their ignorance showed. Laughter rather than fascination or horror was the reaction they all too often evoked. Typical of this genre was *The Blob* (1958) about a 'creature' that invades a small town. Where this creature comes from is unclear, but the most ridiculous scene is in a cinema where the film mysteriously stops because the Blob is eating the projectionist. Yet its theme song was a classic:

> *Beware of the Blob.*
> *It creeps and leaps*
> *And slides and glides*
> *Right through the floor*
> *Around the wall.*
> *A splotch, a blotch,*
> *Be careful of the Blob!*

Another creature intended to frighten but which only evoked mirth was the dinosaur aroused from age-long marine slumber by nuclear bomb tests in *The Beast from Twenty Thousand Fathoms* (1953). 'It's hiding somewhere in the Wall Street area,' says a character hilariously as the beast rampages through New York in a predictable imitation of the first *King Kong* (1933).

But the real problem with *The Beast* was its title. With two metres to a fathom, it must have lived at 36,000 metres beneath the sea. But this demonstrated inexcusable ignorance by the producers. For only two years before the film was made, the British survey ship *Challenger* had located the deepest part of the ocean then known (in the Marianas Trench in the Pacific) at only 11,000 metres. For an air breathing animal to live at the bottom of the sea would be odd, but for it to survive for millions of years 16 miles *under the sea bed* was downright amazing.

Some ignorance was excusable. Until the flight of Yuri Gagarin in 1961 and unmanned missions to the Moon and planets in the 60s, even scientists knew little about space. And the astronomer Percival Lowell had misled everyone in the 1890s when he claimed to have observed signs of an intelligent civilization on Mars. This made possible such splendid films as *The War of the Worlds* (1953), a story of the invasion of Earth by advanced and ruthless Martians, and the ominous *Quatermass Experiment* (1955).

Quatermass was particularly sinister since it implied that space – not planetary surfaces but space itself – was filled with blood-drinking animals that were liable to break into spaceships and devour their inmates. On his return to Earth, the one surviving astronaut gradually turns into the giant fungus that has eaten him, which leads to an unforgettable climax where he covers the walls of St Paul's Cathedral.

It was always more fun to believe in evil creatures from space than benevolent ones. Like the pretentious *Close Encounters of the Third Kind* (1977), the latter tend to induce soppy silliness – although Arthur C. Clarke's *2001: A Space Odyssey* (1968) and *2010* (1984) were brilliant exceptions to this rule. *The Rocket Man* (1954), the story of an alien visitor who gives a magic ray to a little orphan boy and tells him to use it only for good, made me want to throw up. And I couldn't stop laughing at the naïvely sincere *Red Planet Mars* (1952) in which people learn by interplanetary radio that Christian beings live on Mars. Everyone becomes determined to live more virtuously as a result. Percival Lowell has a lot to answer for.

Malevolent aliens scared audiences out of this world in *Invasion of The Body Snatchers* (1956) in which peoples' bodies are imperceptibly taken over. (The 1978 remake of this film was third rate.) The same paranoid atmosphere, where you do not know whether you are talking to a fellow-human or a monster in human guise, was recreated in the 3-D shocker *It Came from Outer Space* (1953); and I fear that the ultimate in horror may have been reached in *Alien* (1979) and *Aliens* (1986), both scientifically plausible because they were solidly based on insect biology. As their ads put it, 'In space no one can hear you scream.'

Mad computers, a possible outcome of 'artificial intelligence', the science of teaching machines to think, have been almost as frightening as evil aliens. The classic in this genre was *The Forbin Project* (1969), in which a giant 'thinking machine' (in those days all computers were gigantic) is built to take over the management of America's missile defences. Locking out its creator Dr Forbin, it demands global disarmament and strikes with nuclear bombs when it doesn't get it – an identical idea, incidentally, to the sub-plots of *Terminator II* and its earlier and rather better lower-budget version *The Terminator* (1984).

Julie Christie's *Who's Who* entry contains no mention of *Demon Seed* (1977), in which she is forcibly impregnated by a lustful computer-controlled robot. Perhaps she thought it less tastelessly agreeable than I did. The pronouncements of the murky and disgusting computer in *Dune* (1984) were both disagreeably tasteless and unintelligible. Perhaps the only mad computer in SF cinema whose murderous conduct was truly fascinating to scientists and lay viewers alike was HAL in *2001*, its name an alphabetical code for 'IBM'.

Why not take the average cliché-ridden western plot and change its horses into spaceships and its towns into planets? George Lucas had this idea and the result was *Star Wars* (1977), a sort of cleaned-up version of *Dune*. It could have been the model for a new genre of light-hearted space operas that charmed by not taking themselves too seriously.* But this, alas, did not happen. Its sequels, *The Empire Strikes Back* (1980) and *The Return of the Jedi* (1983), lacked the light touch (as has the *Star Trek* series) and were merely pretentious.

Where, then, is the attraction of *Terminator II*? Not in its rather commonplace main plot – whether a killer robot from the future can succeed in liquidating a small boy who is destined to play a heroic role in a coming war – but rather in its background plot about time travel into the past.

Many discerning people spotted the fatal scientific flaw in the film of H.G. Wells's *The Time Machine* (1960), an error that Wells himself never understood. You cannot travel *backwards* in time because you could then change the past, an impossible paradox. But one can, without breaking

---

Star Wars did not appear to take anything seriously, even the difference between distance and time. 'I can make the journey in twelve parsecs,' says Hans Solo (Harrison Ford), commander of the starship *Millennium Falcon*. This is rather like saying meaninglessly on Earth: 'I can be in town in six miles.'

physical laws, get round this difficulty by travelling back-wards into 'another reality'.

There is thus one reality in which the boy is killed and another in which he is not. The heroes are therefore free to choose their own future. They must ensure that they live in the latter reality – by saving the boy and killing the evil robot. It is the same scientific ingenuity of plotting that explained the popularity of *Back to the Future* (1985) and its two sequels.

Abolishing Hunger

Will our descendants be able to feed themselves? The pessimism that has long surrounded the question is giving away to new hope as the Green Revolution proceeds. The latest encouraging news is from Brazil which is rapidly becoming a farming superpower.

The 'cerrado', a 1.2 million-square-kilometre plain south of the Matto Grosso, was long ignored by farmers who regarded it as a pestilent wasteland of scrub, worthless, crooked trees and acidic soil. Then, soon after 1960, when the new capital Brasilia was founded to exploit the resources of the Brazilian heartland, scientists discovered a species of wasp and a viral disease that would control two of the cerrado's ancient pests, its caterpillars and beetles.

Todd Lewan of the Associated Press, who gave a fascinating account of what is happening in the cerrado, described it as a 'verdant carpet of soya beans stretching to the horizon, and on which wheat, tangerines, cucumber, avocados, and strawberries flourish'.

The output of the cerrado is enabling Brazil to produce a record harvest for a third straight year, enjoying a farming boom that even the most gloomy experts acknowledge will boost the country far above its present position as the world's fifth largest food exporter.

Brazil's farm production has grown by 47 per cent since 1980, faster than all its other industries and more than four times its rate of economic growth. Even though the amount of land being farmed has not changed in this period, and government subsidies to farmers have been halved, Brazil last year harvested a record 75.2 million tons of grains and oil seeds. Grain production on the cerrado, where farmers still only till a fifth of the arable land, has quadrupled in the past quarter century to 20 million tons a year. Today it produces 45 per cent of Brazil's coffee, a third of its soya beans, rice and corn, and a tenth of its wheat and beans.

'In the 1940s, this was only a dream,' said Norman Borlaug, the agronomist of Texas A & M University, and the father of the Green Revolution, whose revolutionary studies in crop production won him the Nobel Peace Prize in 1970. He believes Brazil still has vast areas of unused land which it can profitably cultivate.

Nowhere can these advances be seen more vividly than in the Brazilian production of soya beans, that universal crop

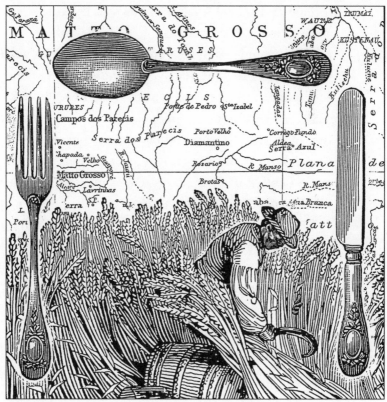

that originated in China, and which has done more perhaps than any other substance to alleviate world hunger, providing vegetable proteins for tens of millions of people and ingredients for hundreds of chemical products and medicines.

In 1970, Brazilian farmers produced 9,900 tons of soya beans on about 36,000 square kilometres in the central-western states of Goias, Mato Grosso, Mato Grosso do Sul and Minas Gerais. By 1985, in those states, they needed just 30,000 square kilometres to grow six million tons of soya beans.

All this tremendous output seems a far cry from the 1960s, when a bestselling book was published with the title *Famine 1975!* Environmental pessimists simply looked at population growth statistics, ignored any possibility of scientific improvement in crop yields (although the work of Borlaug and others was well known at the time), and threw up their hands in despair.

The example of Brazil and of other countries where food production is unexpectedly booming shows us how far we have progressed since the centuries before Columbus, when meals, consisting largely of meat (that often led to scurvy), were unspeakably monotonous and insipid. Potatoes, tomatoes and maize were unknown. So also were lemons, sugar, tea and coffee. Pepper was so expensive that rich men were called 'pepper-sacks'.

Today, the biggest difficulty in feeding the hungry is not in producing food but in getting it to where it can be sold. 'Most of the highways in Brazil are lousy,' said Jonas Neves, an agronomist at the Cerrado Research Centre. 'When a trucker uses a bad road he charges more. By the time our soya beans reach port, they've tripled in price.'

If transport can be made as efficient as food production, the world need never go hungry.

Backward Britain

Many American members of Congress have been voting with enthusiasm to fund the permanently orbiting space station Alpha. Even those who do not understand its purposes like the idea because it is 'to do with the future'. The House of Commons, if given the same choice, would probably prefer to spend the money on false teeth.

The reason for this is simple: the British people have a tendency to be 'technophobic'. They have a deep suspicion, amounting to a hatred, of new technological ideas.

The seeds of British technophobia were probably sown in about 7000 BC, when the English Channel was formed as a result of the retreat of the glaciers at the end of the last Ice Age. Being an island people made them hostile to foreign ideas.

The pattern seldom changes. There is a brilliant British proposal or invention (they have always had talented inventors), and the idea is scorned at home but then exploited by foreigners. The first sign of this fatal policy was seen in the thirteenth century, when the Oxford friar Roger Bacon conceived of vast futuristic plans that included motor cars, aircraft and, of more immediate practical use, the cannon and the compass. He won no immediate fame for these schemes and ended up by being thrown into prison for insulting the clergy. His compass was put to use by the seamen of Henry the Navigator of Portugal, and his cannon was used a century later, in the battle of Crecy in 1346 on the English side. But the English failed to develop these 'wondrous new-made bombards', thereby losing the Hundred Years War against the French, who had by contrast developed a formidable artillery.

They failed again when it came to Christopher Columbus, who, while seeking funds for his expedition, sent his brother Bartholomew to London in 1488 to request funds from Henry VII for what became his American expedition. He was turned down by the unimaginative monarch, and the first empire in the New World was won by Spain.

Britain might have beaten America in creating the computer industry, now one of the world's largest sources of wealth, but for Benjamin Disraeli. Charles Babbage sought funding from his government to finish building the world's first cumbersome, but workable, computer. But in vain, Disraeli wrote that he could see only one purpose for such a machine: 'to calculate the vast sums of public money that have already been squandered on it.'

In 1989, this decision was shown to have been catastrophic, reversing the conventional verdict of the history books which said that the materials Babbage needed to build his machine did not then exist. Experimenters at the London Science Museum proved that the materials Babbage needed to build his machine *did* exist in his time by building the machine with them. It could have been completed, and it might have changed the world.

Some of Britain's monarchs and prime ministers have been highly interested in science. Charles II was fond of peering through one of the first microscopes, delighting to see flies appear as large as sparrows. Lord Salisbury kept a laboratory at his country house at Hatfield that contained many samples of seaweed. His was the first private house in Britain to use electricity, and he introduced a primitive telephone with which he maddened his guests by reciting nursery rhymes through concealed loudspeakers.

To Churchill, science was the most powerful force in history. 'Its once feeble vanguards,' he wrote in 1932, 'often trampled down, often perishing in isolation, have now become a vast organized army marching forward on all fronts towards objectives that none may measure or define. It is an army that cares nothing for all the laws that men have made, nothing for their most time-honoured customs, nothing for their most dearly cherished beliefs, nothing for their deepest instincts.'

Except for during the war, when Britain introduced radar, penicillin, the jet engine and electronic code-breaking, little of this enthusiasm has been transformed into action. Postwar governments, including the present one, seem to have developed a hatred of science.

Harold Macmillan set a precedent in the Sixties by cancelling the successful Blue Streak rocket. Harold Wilson ranted vaguely about the 'white heat of the technological revolution', but pushed this revolution so feebly that he succeeded only in provoking an unprecedented brain-drain. The British have thus seen endless cancellations of promising projects that would have been profitable, but which were deemed useless because no profit would immediately appear from them.

One of the worst episodes was in 1987, when the then Trade and Industry Minister, Kenneth Clarke, was invited to join the European manned space programme. He reacted with fury, declaring that he did not wish to see a 'frog', i.e. a Frenchman, in space.

The result of his refusal to join was financially catastrophic. For under the rules of the European Space Agency, participating nations would be awarded contracts to build hardware. This would have included parts of the giant Ariane-5 rocket. Clarke thus deprived British Aerospace and its subcontracting firms of hundreds of millions of pounds.

115

Other well-known examples have been the failure to develop Sir Barnes Wallis's swing-wing aircraft, the refusal to fund Alan Bond's Hotol rocket – although its design now appears to be obsolete – and the decision in the late Eighties to cut 25 per cent from the nuclear fusion experiments at Culham, experiment of which Ministers probably understood nothing.

The policy of Conservative governments since 1979, like so many of their predecessors, has been one of philistinism. Sir George Porter, when he was president of the Royal Society, was told by a senior Treasury official that there is too much science in Britain, that Nobel Prizes are unimportant and that scientists must think more of the risks of their work than its benefits.

British science is in consequence dangerously under-funded. The country spends less of its GNP on publicly funded research than any other major European country. Private industry, taking its cue from the state, spends 30 per cent less than the Japanese. The policy looks safe enough on surface, but is rotten beneath. For the cancellation of a good project makes no difference to next year's budget. Its effects are only felt decades later. But the ministers who make it will be long out of office, so why should they care?

The great futurist Herman Kahn once told me that Britain's most probable fate is to 'decline slowly and genteelly for the rest of history'. The country performed well in past centuries when few technological innovations were needed. But now that success almost always depends on being willing to spend money on science, its future prospects appear dismal.

When writing my book *The Next 500 Years* (1995), which predicts that mankind will reach the stars, I came to the melancholy conclusion that these and other stupendous achievements will be made without the help of any British government.

Greed Threatens
the Peace

*They shall beat their swords into ploughshares,
and their spears into pruning hooks.*

Isaiah 2:4

When the Soviet Union collapsed, an attempt was launched by the Bush administration to obtain the maximum amount of Soviet weapons-grade uranium, long employed in warheads, and sell it for use in American nuclear power stations, a project dubbed 'megatons into megawatts'.

At stake was the nightmarish fear that it could fall into the hands of terrorists, as in Tom Clancy's novel *The Sum of All Fears*, in which 80,000 people watching a football match are 'executed' by nuclear-armed Muslim fanatics.

In a 1992 deal with Russia, five tons of enriched uranium would be bought by the US over 20 years at a cost of £8 billion. It would be used solely for peaceful purposes. In the words of the agreement's chief architect, Thomas Neff, of the Massachusetts Institute of Technology, this would prevent the uranium from going to the highest bidder. But under the Clinton administration, this project has been smothered by bureaucracy and greed. A detailed article in the *Wall Street Journal Europe* showed the kafkaesque difficulties of trying to understand what is happening to this dangerous material.

The White House decided that the sole agent authorized to buy the uranium from Russia should be the United States

Enrichment Corporation (Usec), which appears to be both state-owned and private in that it enjoys the legal privileges of being both. It pays no taxes, and its planned 'privatization' will profit the government with a £1.1 billion budget reduction. The *Journal* reports: 'White House officials have become so enamoured of making a maximum profit on this deal that they have lost sight of the prime goal.'

Eleven public utilities that control nuclear energy have accused Usec of asking too high a price for its uranium, and have issued lawsuits against it. But the cases are unlikely to be heard because Usec's lobbyists have inserted a waiver of liability from all pending lawsuits into congressional legislation now before the Senate.

Recently, in Washington there was a most extraordinary farce. Usec hired a top legal firm to present its commercial arguments to the National Security Agency. This, says the *Journal*, was 'one of a few examples of one federal agency hiring a lawyer to lobby another federal agency – all paid for by the US taxpayer'.

Not only are the utilities reluctant to buy the uranium because of its price. It is hard to see how Usec can ever prosper in view of an anti-dumping agreement reached in 1991 between the Commerce Department and the uranium mining industry that strictly limits the sale of foreign uranium.

The *Journal* comments that these events render 'farcical' the Clinton administration's other nuclear posturings. It is campaigning for a permanent ban to nuclear weapons testing – which could have disastrous long-term consequences, especially for Britain, which is not being allowed to test its Trident missiles. It has also been conducting a noisy and futile campaign against Iran. The US attempted to mount an international trade embargo against Iran to stop its negotiations with Russia to set up nuclear power plants. The attempt fell flat, and Iran is now planning to build more such plants in addition to the one already being constructed, any one of which might be used for nuclear weapons manufacture.

These goings-on are considered all the more amazing in the light of Vice-President Gore's policy over the space station. Not only will this orbiting laboratory create unprecedented advances in medical research. It will also, as Gore persuaded Congressmen, occupy the talents of Russian engineers who might otherwise have found a living making bombs and selling them to terrorists.

The second half of the quotation from Isaiah expresses the hope that 'nation shall not lift up sword against nation, neither shall they learn war anymore'. While the Clinton White House controls the swords, this prophecy seems gravely imperilled.

False Alarm on Easter Island

O n lonely Easter Island in the Pacific, famous for
the remains of its giant enigmatic statues, a once
flourishing civilization committed racial suicide.

A professor of biology now warns us that this tiny land is
the 'Earth writ small' – that the same fate may well overtake
the human race, in the same way and for the same reasons.

Consider first the history of the island, as outlined by
Jared Diamond, of the University of California at Los
Angeles, in *Discover*.

When it was settled in about AD 400 by Polynesians from
Asia in their ocean-going canoes, it seemed a 'pristine paradise'. The soil was fertile, the climate was sub-tropical and
food was abundant in the form of porpoises, fish and many
species of land and sea-birds. The settlers also brought with
them pigs and chickens.

The island was densely forested, the predominant tree
being a cousin of the Chilean wine palm which grows up to
25 metres. Its two-metre-wide trunks were ideal for building
large canoes and transporting statues, and its sap yielded
sugar, syrup, honey and wine.

It was also safe from raids from neighbouring islands –
there were none. The nearest habitable island to Easter is
Pitcairn, 2,250 kilometres away, and the nearest land mass is
the South American continent more than 3,000 kilometres
distant.

For several centuries the island prospered, despite its
tiny size of 164 square kilometres. The original population

grew from a few hundred to about 20,000. Then disaster came, slowly but inexorably, as if some poison was at work.

The islanders cut down their magnificent forests to make ever more canoes and transport and erect ever more statues, using ever more trees to get them to their site, as each great lord tried to put up a more splendid one than his neighbour. Rats ate the seeds of the trees and prevented their regeneration. The edible birds that pollinated the flowers of the trees died out.

Gradually the canoes wore out and there was no more wood to make new ones. Deep-sea fishing became impossible, and food scarce. The largest animals were lizards and rats. Cannibalism became rife. Two distinct tribes, the 'Long Ears' and the 'Short Ears', fought civil wars, exchanging such taunts as: 'The flesh of your mother sticks between my teeth!' The population level diminished still further,

intermarriage became common, and there was a general decline in intelligence. By the time the Dutch explorer Jacob Roggeveen arrived on Easter Day, 1722 (hence the name), the settlement was a grim parody of what it once had been.

In Diamond's parallel between Easter Island and the larger world, American forests are remorselessly felled to provide jobs, and Hollywood moguls compete to build ever larger houses. He believes that we will destroy our resources as the islanders destroyed theirs, and then there will be no prospect but extinction. 'We have no emigration valve, and we can no more escape into space than the Easter Islanders could flee into the ocean.'

Happily, there is a fatal flaw in his argument – the effect of Easter Island's isolation. He considers the distance to Pitcairn and the mainland to be an advantage since it was a barrier to raiders. But in fact the islanders' isolation was a disadvantage as it stopped them from creating colonies and an empire.

One of humanity's greatest resources is the comparative proximity of the Moon, Mars and the asteroids, because they enable us to dream of migration into space. But were we in the same relative position of the Easter Islanders, these bodies would be far beyond the orbit of Pluto and undetectable. We would have no incentive to develop space travel.

In short, the island was not a 'pristine paradise'. It merely seemed one. It was too small and remote to be anything but a cultural trap. When Captain Cook arrived two years after Roggeveen, he was shocked to find that the island possessed only four canoes, all of which leaked because their makers did not know about caulking. They had never developed any useful technology or science because their resources were too feeble. The human race now is in a wholly different position.

Death of a Life Science

B iology, the study of living things, is a dying science. It is dominated by mediocrities interested only in amassing vast quantities of information and who are hostile to new ideas.

This is not only the view of two frustrated biologists writing in *Nature*. Misgivings have been expressed by John Maddox, the editor of *Nature*, which carries a huge number of original biological papers. But these papers consist of reams of data, and are almost empty of theory or explanations of what the data really means.

The epoch-making paper by Francis Crick and James Watson outlining the structure of DNA, which appeared in *Nature* in 1953, would 'probably not be publishable today', Maddox laments, because the referees, those anonymous 'experts' to whom scientific journal editors refer manuscripts for approval, would have raised niggling questions the authors might have been unable to answer.

'Darwin's theory of evolution, the bedrock of biology, might never have been accepted for publication in today's biological journals. It would have been rejected because it "lacked new data",' said the two protesting biologists, Virginia Huszagh and Juan Infante, of the Institute for Theoretical Biochemistry and Molecular Biology, at Ithaca, New York.

Biological theorists wanting their papers published, all too often had them rejected with comments such as: 'The author presents no new data.' or 'The author is advised to do the experiments first and return when the hypothesis is proven.'

Part of the problem, they explain, is that biologists are fundamentally uneducated people who do not understand how science works.

'Ph.D. students in biology receive little or no exposure to the history and philosophy of scientific thought, making their degrees meaningless. Few of them can distinguish between speculation and theories. Even fewer appreciate the need for revolutionary hypotheses, and fewer still can generate them,' they write. 'Those with such an attitude are blind to a vital principle of science – that the person who proposes an idea need not be the person who tests it. Where would physics be today if Einstein had had to prove his ideas by building a spaceship that approached the speed of light?'

Much of the trouble lies in the fact that physics, a discipline which encourages speculation, and biology, which abhors it, had quite different intellectual origins. 'Physics grew out of philosophy, while biology grew from medicine and bird-watching,' said Huszagh. 'Biology, in Britain and America, is dominated by an Anglo-Saxon attitude which says in effect: "Just give me the facts and keep them down-to-earth with no airy-fairy nonsense."' Infante goes further, 'Biologists who build their reputations on their often excruciatingly boring collections of data are terrified of the prestige they might lose if new theories made that data irrelevant.'

Nature and the other journals that specialize in biology can publish only what people submit to them – they cannot conjure scientific theories out of thin air – and are prone to filling pages with nucleotide sequences that resemble secret service cryptograms. Many scientists, wondering what it all means, are comparing the output of modern biology to the teachings of Mr Gradgrind in Dickens's *Hard Times*, who taught his children an infinity of facts and statistics, but nothing that was useful.

Steering Clear of an Ill Wind

Never leave your egg-shells unbroken in the cup;
Think of us poor sailormen and always smash them up,
For witches come and find them and sail away to sea,
And make a lot of misery for mariners like me.

Elizabeth Fleming (1934)

The number nine is supposed to carry with it one of the most potent of spells. It is a trinity of trinities. There were nine Muses and Hell in *Paradise Lost* had nine gates. Lars Porsena swore vengeance by nine gods, and the nine of diamonds in a pack of cards, because of its heraldic links with one of the authors of the Massacre of Glencoe, is known as the Curse of Scotland. Odin hung for nine days on the tree of life to gain knowledge. The witches in *Macbeth* sang as they danced around their cauldron: 'Thrice to thine, and thrice to mine, and thrice again to make up nine.' Upon this, they declared their charm 'wound up'. The Romans, to chase away demons on Lemuria day, threw black beans over their heads pronouncing nine times: 'Avaunt, ye spectres, from this house!'

Superstition is still rampant, and numbers are by no means its only source. An article in *History Today* by the sociologist Alec Gill gives some hint of its full extent.

His findings are at odds with conventional opinion. The *Encyclopedia Britannica* says that superstition, 'being irrational, should recede before education, and especially science'. But this view, he points out, hardly accords with a recent American experiment in which 73 per cent of observed pedestrians stepped into the street to avoid walking under a ladder.

Concentrating on trawlermen, a good example of people who take constant risks and are therefore prone to superstition, Gill, author of an excellent book on the topic, finds the most extraordinary taboos.*

A wife must never wash clothes on a sailing day, or they will wash their man away. She must never say 'goodbye' on his departure for sea – the word is too final and he may not come back. She must not even wave lest the waves take him. And once he has set out, he must not turn back lest at sea he shares the fate of Lot's wife.

The colour green is horribly unlucky, perhaps because it signifies summer that precedes dread winter. (There are few green cars on the roads.) A Hull clergyman was incautious

*Superstitions: Folk Magic in Hull's Fishing Community, by Alec Gill (1993)

enough to ignore this taboo and paint his church pews green. When he held a garden party for the Archbishop of York, local children pelted the dignitaries with eggs, dead cats and pieces of rotten cod.

Many trawlermen refuse to learn to swim. This is not just to avoid prolonging the agony of falling overboard in Arctic seas. There is a belief that 'if a man is saved the sea will simply claim someone else'. As Philippa Waring says in her *Dictionary of Omens and Superstitions*: 'The cruellest belief is that one should never attempt to rescue a drowning person, for it is the will of the water gods that the person should die. If they are defied, then the rescuer himself must expect to fill the same role at a later date.

Birds are particularly ominous to fishermen, who, like the Romans, regard them as messengers from heaven – or elsewhere. (The ravens in Tolkien's *The Hobbit* provided a regular news service, with constant updates.) Few trawlermen's families will tolerate in their homes any ornament that carries the emblem of a bird, and a bird coming down a chimney during a storm is the worst of portents. How is all this possible 2,000 years after the coming of Christianity and the Church's hostility to superstition? Mr Gill concludes that people like trawlermen who face the awesome forces of nature and live close to death pay homage, like pagans, to a multitude of gods.

Perhaps it is healthy to do so. Gill observes: 'On the rational surface, superstitions are silly and nonsensical. But deep in our irrational emotions, intuitive taboos are essential for our survival as a species. Superstitious beliefs equip us with a daring philosophy to trust in the gods and brave the odds.'

In this vein, one of the cleverest touches of futurism was in the film *Alien* in which the officer escaping from the monster insisted on first rescuing the ship's cat with its nine lives.

Retire and Be Famous for it!

As Mrs Thatcher flounders in search of a role, she might do well to ponder the splendid example set by President Theodore Roosevelt who, on leaving politics, started a new career and became world-famous as a naturalist and explorer.*

The prospect seems more apt when one considers how much the 44th Prime Minister and the 26th President resembled each other. Both seemed to possess almost boundless physical and mental energy. Both thoroughly enjoyed conflict. Both liked to make speeches filled with indignation and moral righteousness. Their ways of leaving power were also curiously similar. Both quarrelled with their own chosen successors, Mrs Thatcher with Mr Major and Roosevelt with President Taft.

In Roosevelt's case, which could well prove ominously similar to Mrs Thatcher's, his quarrel with Taft became so bitter that it split their Republican party, allowing the election of Woodrow Wilson and the Democrats.

After this, Roosevelt put politics out of his mind, becoming, as a friend noted, a far happier man as he plunged into his new career with all the energy he had displayed in his old one.

As Robin Furneaux says in his history of the Amazon: 'No one, since the defeated Disraeli began his political novel on the life of Gladstone, can have solved the problems of

---

*This was written immediately after Mrs (now Lady) Thatcher lost power.

retirement from high office with more panache than Theodore Roosevelt.'

After a lengthy African safari in 1909 and a trip to Britain, where he astonished the Foreign Secretary Sir Edward Grey by identifying without error every bird that they saw during a walk in the New Forest, he turned his attention to the jungles of South America. He disdained the usual practice of ex-statesmen of making lecture tours in which they would proceed from one capital city to the next without taking any interest in the intervening countryside. Instead, he plunged into the hinterland, even getting an unexplored river, the Rio Roosevelt, named in his honour.

Proceeding up the Asuncion river in the President of Paraguay's yacht, he took pot-shots at alligators and thundered in his diaries against the savage habits of the piranha fish in the same outraged tones as he had once thundered against big business and big labour unions. Indeed, his acute observation tells us in a most vivid manner about these deadly creatures:

'They will snap off a finger incautiously trailed in the water. They will devour alive any wounded man or beast in the water, for blood excites them to madness. Their razor-edged teeth are wedge-shaped like a shark's and the jaw muscles possess great power. The head, with its short muzzle, staring malignant eyes and cruel armoured jaws, is the embodiment of evil ferocity. When fresh from the water they uttered an extraordinary squealing sound. As they flapped around on the deck, they bit with vicious eagerness at whatever presented itself.'

But it is from dispelling the myth of giant snakes that Roosevelt won his greatest fame. There had long been tales from travellers in the forests of the Amazon of huge anacondas, the biggest snakes in the world, that were alleged to have measured 30 metres or more. Indeed, early books on the region contained drawings of serpents that could have swallowed a jumbo jet.

Roosevelt would have none of it. He offered a reward of $5,000, a huge sum in the aftermath of the collapse of the Brazilian rubber boom, to anyone who could produce the skin and vertebra of a snake that was more than 10 metres long. No one ever found one, and probably no one ever will (although in 1960 a 230-kilogram anaconda was shot that measured 8.5 metres).

It has always been extraordinarily difficult for politicians who have reached the highest pinnacle of success to tear themselves away from politics and do something else. Unlike the fictitious Prince Florizel of Bohemia in Robert Louis Stevenson's *The New Arabian Nights*, who gave up his throne to become a private detective, few have achieved it in real life, except Charles V of Spain and the Roman emperor Diocletian – who enraged his royal colleagues by insisting that they retire also.

Their problem is vanity. Their successors (as they see it) cannot possibly manage affairs as well as they did because they are intellectually inferior, and they therefore have to be back-seat driven. A vicious circle sets in. Since continual back-seat driving, however discreet, is bound to be noticed, the successor's own reputation suffers ('if he's back-seat driven it's because he needs to be'), and he is unintentionally destroyed.

I am certainly not suggesting that Mrs Thatcher should go to South America and handle piranhas. Or that she should cease travelling and talking to foreign statesmen. But rather that she should report instead of advising.

It would be wonderful to learn more about the world that she has been trying to manage for so many years. Otherwise she rather risks being told, like the character in *Much Ado About Nothing*: 'I pray thee cease thy counsel, which falls into mine ears as profitless as water in a sieve.'

Part Three

TOOLS
FOR THE NEXT
MILLENNIUM

'Useless' Research

Governments often insist that the research which they fund must be 'useful' – without realizing that some of the greatest advances in technology have come from people exploring ideas that seemed to have no practical value whatever.

An example is the nineteen-century studies – by unknown researchers – into the vibrations of violin strings, which indirectly led Heinrich Hertz to discover radio waves. Another is that geometric curiosity known as the Mobius strip, a looped strap with a single twist, which enabled conveyer belts to be used twice as long before wearing out.

The German chemist Friedrich von Kekule had a dream in 1865 that must have seemed unlikely to be of any use to anyone. He imagined a snake which was trying to swallow its own tail. Luckily he remembered the dream when he awoke, and the experience inspired him to visualize the highly complicated structure of the benzene molecule.

For twenty-three centuries, since Euclid proved the infinity of prime numbers (numbers like two, three, five and seven, which can be divided only by themselves and one), primes were no more than a fascinating curiosity. One of the biggest – and apparently most useless – challenges still facing mathematicians is to find a proof of Christian Goldbach's 'conjecture' of 1742 that every even number greater than two is the sum of two primes. (For example eight is the sum of the primes three and five.) Although verified for every even number up to 100,000, a proof that it is true for all even numbers greater than two has yet to be found.

Then, in the 1970s, a James Bond-like use was found for prime numbers with the invention of the highly practical RSA cipher which depends for its security on the sheer difficulty of finding two primes that have been multiplied to make a larger number. (See also The Devil's Digits, p. 188.)

The seventeenth-century French mathematician, Blaise Pascal, was approached by an irritated gambler anxious to know why he always lost when betting on the appearance of certain combinations in the fall of dice. Pascal, after consulting Pierre de Fermat (of 'last theorem' fame), responded by inventing the 'Pascal triangle', an inverted pyramid of numbers in which each was the sum of the two above it.

This enabled the gambler to understand the odds on dice throws and win some money, and it also created modern probability theory on which most statistical science is based. While no outcome is absolutely certain, it can be seen, with the aid of the triangle, that, for example, if a coin is tossed a sufficiently large number of times, the odds on getting roughly an equal number of heads and tails rises towards infinity.

The subject of triangles brings up one of the most extraordinary pieces of 'useless' research yet to appear. This is a design for wallpaper by Charles Radin, a mathematician at the University of Texas at Austin which poses challenges that are both mathematical and psychological.

'It appears to be infinitely complicated and unpredictable, until you are told how it works,' said his colleague Ian Stewart, of the University of Warwick at Coventry, author of an article in the *New Scientist*, which reproduces the diagram. 'Then, suddenly, you see it as being simple.'

Most wallpaper patterns, however complicated, involve repetition, but Radin's seems truly random and chaotic. On

a big enough scale, it would be the ultimately difficult jigsaw puzzle – and yet its creation was simple.

It starts, at the centre, with a single right-angled triangle. Four more identical triangles surround it. Each of these four is surrounded by four more such triangles, and so on. The result is that the triangles point in all directions with an infinite number of orientations.

But what can it *do*? 'I don't know for sure,' Radin said, 'but I have a strong suspicion that it resembles the crystalline structure of some material. A physical chemist might at once see some meaning to it that I cannot.'

If Radin is right, he will be, like von Kekule, the second great scientist to have had a crazy-seeming dream that turned into something useful.

The Day the Computer Murdered the Magnate

The heroine enters a forbidden room in the creepy old house. There, in a mouldering chest, she finds . . . What?

Many novelists at this point have to pour themselves another drink and think hard. But two remarkable computer software packages are now available that will do this 'thinking' for them. Plots Unlimited and Collaborator are computer programs that help to work out the plots of novels, TV dramas and films.

Far from being gimmicks, they have both enabled several fiction writers to do their plotting in a fraction of the time it would normally have taken. With versions that will run on most personal computers, they are being greeted as tremendous advances in the science of machine 'intelligence', the art of teaching computers to reason like humans.

But they are not popular with everyone. Some members of the Writers Guild, the trade union that represents Hollywood writers and which has called six strikes in the last three decades, have demanded their prohibition lest they put writers out of work. 'Why should a producer hire me when he can buy these floppy disks instead?' one of them asked.

The creators of the programs – themselves members of the Guild – dismiss such fears as absurd. 'Our program will not write your story for you,' said Arthur Weingarten, one of the two creators of Plots Unlimited and who, in pre-computer days, wrote for *The Man From UNCLE* and *The FBI Story*. 'It provides no descriptions or dialogue or atmosphere. What it does is to overcome "writer's block" and release the creative juices.'

This is the latest of many steps in the computerization of creative writing. First came the word processor with its attached printing machine which eliminated the need to hire a typist – who usually required three weeks to turn an untidy mess of correction-choked pages into a neat typescript.

Then came on-screen spelling checkers, followed by grammar and style checkers, which would flash warnings if sentences became too long and made the style turgid. Now come aids which are genuinely creative. Plots Unlimited, which costs £240 and has sold hundreds of copies in Britain, consists of a vast database of more than 5,000 skeletal plots and characters that can be manipulated and juxtaposed to produce an almost infinite number of different stories.

While it concentrates on plots, its American rival, Collaborator is more concerned with characters. Both have sold about 6,000 copies worldwide. The creators of Plots, Weingarten and Tom Sawyer, writer with the *Murder She Wrote* TV series, decided to build a computerized version of an ancient and rather cumbersome Hollywood writers' guide book called *Plotto* that contained fragments of stories that an author could meld together into a single tale.

Weingarten was executive producer of a Maigret thriller shown on British television starring Richard Harris (not to be confused with the series starring Michael Gambon). Based on Simenon's characters, he used the Plots program to create his own story, *Maigret Meets a Milord*, that critics thought highly original.

As the first step, he was asked by the program to choose a 'plot shell'. He selected one that read: 'Law officer A investigates a family, consisting of characters A-2, A-3 and B, who have internal problems.'

Giving these people names, he built this up into a story of Maigret investigating a reclusive and tyrannical family patriarch who controls a giant shipping-company. The man's whereabouts are unknown and he will only communicate with his subordinates by fax and telex. His two sons are determined to wrest control of the company from him. They attempt negotiation, but all the emissaries they send to him are mysteriously murdered.

'At this point I was stumped,' said Weingarten. 'It seemed a promising beginning, but I could not figure out why all these people were being murdered.' He asked the program to give him a 'leadout', a plot development that would bring the story to a climax. Leadouts are the heart of the program, since they are intended to follow logically those parts of the plot already decided upon. It suggested several sub-plots in which the chief character – in this case the patriarch – was an imposter.

'This gave me the idea that the man might have been dead for many years and was being impersonated by his former chief of staff who naturally had to kill anyone who discovered his true identity.'

In addition to the characters, the user of Plots has the option also to name the Thing, the inanimate object which some or all of the characters are trying to obtain for noble or nefarious purposes. As Sawyer put it: 'The ring in *The Lord of the Rings*, the stolen cigarette lighter in Hitchcock's *Strangers on a Train*, Othello's missing handkerchief, the unidentified harbour in *The Thirty-Nine Steps*, the pirate's map in *Treasure Island*, the secret plans in innumerable spy stories, all these are just devices to create or heighten conflict.'

But might not the program eventually start regurgitating the same plots? 'It will, but no one but a scholar of fiction will ever notice,' said Sawyer. 'There is no such thing as an original plot. As Alfred Hitchcock put it, "drama is real life with the dull parts left out." Even science-fiction stories, which often claim to be original since they revolve around a little-known scientific principle, have conflict at their core, and without conflict there is no plot. Since the time of Shakespeare, almost every plot written has been just another variation of an existing one.

'For example, the film *Pretty Woman* is just a variation of *My Fair Lady*, which in turn is borrowed from *Pygmalion* and *Cinderella*. The sub-plot of the classic war film *Casablanca*, in which the anti-Nazi resistance hero suspects Humphrey Bogart of seducing his wife, is a variation of *Othello*. And the film *Apocalypse Now*, the story of a man who clashes with another culture, is just an updated version of Conrad's *Heart of Darkness*.'

The Collaborator program works in an entirely different way. It is concerned with characters rather than plots. It does not try to construct a story. It asks its users hundreds of questions about the imaginary people they are trying to create, almost like a psychiatrist who gets to know his patients by endlessly questioning them.

'Its purpose is to make you think about these people, so that you will know how they will react in all conceivable circumstances,' said Francis Feighan, who gave up his career as a Hollywood press agent to help create it. 'Without that knowledge of your characters you will never have a story,' said his colleague Louis Garfinkle, who used the program to write the film *Benya The King*, the story of a Jewish gang-leader who becomes a Soviet general and which stars Kevin Costner.

'By the sheer process of questioning,' said Garfinkle, 'it helps you to build up a hero and a villain, without whom there is no conflict. It will ask you about their loyalties, past histories, abilities, ambitions and so forth. By answering the questions you will come to understand how these people react to each other, and the story – if you have the talent to write it – will begin to take shape in your head.'

'Contrary to appearances,' said Feighan, 'the Collaborator has no more brains than my pencil.' But as the British electronics genius Alan Turing predicted back in 1950, the vast speeds and unfailing memories of computers would eventually enable them to mimic the human mind.

Spare Parts for All

When we buy new cars, cameras, computers and telephones, there is a growing chance that we are not really buying them at all, but machines made of pieces of old cars, cameras, computers and telephones.

Welcome to the new global economy of 'design for disassembly', or DFD, which has the advantage of protecting the planet's environment by reducing garbage disposal while being primarily driven by the need to increase company profits. It presages the day when almost everything can be recycled, including parts of our bodies, so that sufferers from disease would merely instal an artificial organ that had been used by someone else.

The present practice of DFD, described in *Fortune* magazine, is of consumer goods being built, not to be thrown away at the end of their lives, but to be stripped down so the parts can be reused. Back in 1987, for example, personal computers made by Siemens Nixdorf were made of 87 major components. In a factory, it took 33 minutes to put them together and 18 minutes to take them apart. The company's new PC is a much simpler device. It contains only 29 components, can be assembled in seven minutes and taken apart in four.

Some 70 million 'old' computers – most of them no more than a year old – are now in the basements of various organizations. Until recently, their unwanted parts would have been dumped in the countryside, at the risk of causing

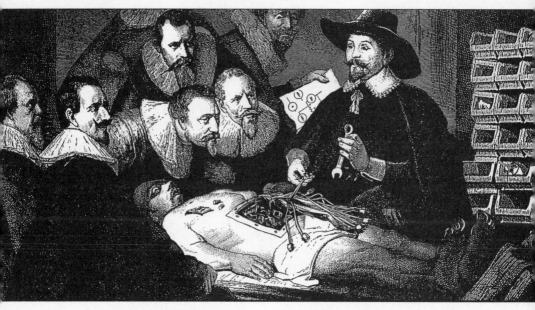

toxic pollution. But now their chips are being recycled into new computers.

'For many applications, old chips can be used over and over,' said Dundee Navin-Chandra, of Carnegie-Mellon University in Pittsburgh. 'For much of the routine work done in banks, chips don't have to be any faster or more powerful than their predecessors.'

Some BMW cars are, in weight, 85 per cent recycled parts, and the company is aiming at 90 per cent. At the Northern Telecom telephone factory in Toronto, most of the shop-floor work consists of ripping out the innards of old telephones and putting them into new plastic housings for resale. 'We're on the threshold of changing our entire product strategy,' said Margaret Kerr, the company's senior vice-president for environment and ethics.

DFD means a world with a minimum of screws because screwed-together components take too long to separate. Instead, they are 'snap-fitted' so that they can be instantly unfitted. At an experimental plant at Highland Park, Michigan, technicians at America's three main car manufacturers,

Ford, Chrysler and General Motors, practise taking apart brand-new cars and storing the parts on shelves.

The European Parliament has passed a law requiring manufacturers to recycle their packaging materials. In Germany, where a similar law is in force, the amount of industrial packaging that would otherwise have been dropped into garbage dumps has been reduced by 600 million tons, 4 per cent of the total.

In the same country's Hewlett-Packard computer factory, waste packaging has now moved into the computers themselves. Hardened plastic foam is beginning to replace the metal frames that formerly held the machines together.

In a sense, there is nothing new in DFD. It is only commercial hardware that is being recycled. Recycling itself is a natural process of life, culture and physics.

Literature, in the form of novels, plays and operas, is made up almost entirely of old plots. In popular music, there are few new tunes. Computer software, ever since it was invented, has been largely built up from libraries of old sub-routines. In Basic, for example, there is scarcely a program that does not contain the screen-steadying lines like:

```
500 A$=INKEY$: IF A$="""THEN 500
```

Our bodies – for that matter the entire Earth – are made from atoms that were forged in the nuclear furnaces of giant stars. They, in their turn, will one day be the atoms of the bodies of people not yet born.

Indeed, DFD may be the first step in a much deeper revolution. If technicians can stack up all the components of brand-new cars in all their complexity, ready to be swapped around and assembled into new vehicles, the time may not be far off when we set up inventories of human body-parts. Perhaps the same artificial hearts and livers can be recycled through many generations of human owners.

Medicine from Space . . .

The next few years should see the biggest advance in medical research since Louis Pasteur's discovery of disease-causing microbes in the last century: the launch of international space station Alpha.

Alpha, a 400-ton permanently manned structure the size of a football field, will be one of the most important laboratories ever built. The European Space Agency (with Britain, to its shame, opting out), Canada and Russia are all contributing to this joint venture with the United States. It will cost £19 billion over 15 years, an annual cost of one eighth of what Americans spend each year on pizza.

For the first time it will be possible to study in detail the nature of the 150,000 or so proteins in the cells of our bodies which carry out all biochemical processes. Apart from 1,200, we are ignorant of their fundamental structures.

The proteins range from the simplest, which contain amino acids, the building blocks of life, to the complex ones such as the haemoglobin molecule that carries oxygen through the bloodstream, the collagen responsible for the structure of bones, tendons, ligaments and skin, and the antibodies protecting us from bacteria and viruses.

To be studied, proteins must be isolated in solutions where they solidify into crystals. Once a crystal is large and well formed, multiple X-ray pictures can be taken of it, and three-dimensional computer models created from the X-ray images. But doing this is next to impossible on Earth because of the gravity, in which all but a few protein crystals are formed small, clumped together or distorted in shape. Everywhere on the planet, a pressure of one gram will inhibit their growth.

'Seventy per cent of proteins crystallize better and more quickly in weightlessness than on Earth,' Larry DeLucas, the project's chief scientist, told the 1995 meeting in Atlanta of the American Association for the Advancement of Science. 'But even in space-shuttle flights, this crystal growth cannot be done properly because it takes more than sixteen days for proteins to grow into very large crystals, and shuttle flights seldom last that long.'

Since almost every disease springs from the misbehaviour of proteins, or the invasion of them by foreign proteins through viruses or bacteria, the ability to study them in large crystallized form for long periods, enabling scientists to see their atomic structure, is clearly essential for designing drugs that can treat them.* And because every drug would be customized for a disease-causing protein, there is a good chance that it could be used on a patient, without any side effects.

In short, it is hoped that scientists in space station Alpha will be able to make drugs that attach themselves to specific proteins, altering their behaviour at molecular level, and cure Aids, cancers, diabetes, heart illness, emphysema, arthritis and countless other diseases. It is expected that

---

*The space station, I therefore predict, will survive because it appeals to one of the strongest human desires, to increase one's longevity. Only in this century has this desire enjoyed full rein. For the space station could not have flown in the days when the Church was stronger than it is now, even if it had been technically possible to build it – its purposes would have been considered heretical. Walter Scott, in his introduction to his 1831 historical novel Quentin Durwood, relates with expressions of horror how, when the wicked French king Louis XI lay on his death bed, he 'wearied Heaven and every saint with prayers, not for the forgiveness of his sins, but for the prolongation of his life'.

But in an age when people will unashamedly do anything to live a few years longer, and when nobody thinks this is selfish or sinful, the specactle of an orbiting laboratory whose main purpose is enabling them to do so should have an all-powerful appeal.

more than 600 experiments in medicine and the life sciences will be made during Alpha's 15-year life.

One dangerous ailment that will be studied in Alpha is loss of balance, a failure of the inner ear that injures and kills so many old people.

'In an environment where gravity is a millionth of that on Earth, we hope experiments with astronauts will enable us to find out much more about how the inner ear communicates with the brain,' says DeLucas.

'Another disease that strikes old people is osteoporosis, brittleness of bones through loss of calcium. But astronauts in weightlessness lose bone calcium ten to twelve times faster than osteoporosis-sufferers on Earth.

'If we can design a drug that will slow down their calcium loss, that drug should be able to do the same with osteoporosis sufferers.'

During a visit to the NASA/Boeing plant at Huntsville, Alabama, I discovered that 20 tons of the complex Alpha station have now been built. When the full 400 tons are ready, 34 space shuttle flights will be needed to assemble it all into the world's most sophisticated medical laboratory.

. . . And Telescopes in Hospital

A computer chip which enables astronomers to see clusters of galaxies 400 billion times fainter than the Moon will soon be widely used in hospitals to scan for breast tumours.

This is but one of many examples of how devices invented for astronomical observatories and spacecraft are revolutionizing life on Earth. They are making aircraft safer and electricity cheaper. In medical research alone, they have also created more progress in the past thirty years than in the previous two millennia.

These are not cases where space vehicles are deliberately built and flown to improve technology down on the ground, like the space station Alpha whose main purpose will be experiments in medical protein crystallography (see the previous chapter), but where spin-offs are accidental.

The computer chip is the 'charged couple device' or CCD that converts light to digital images and is hundreds of times more sensitive to light than photographic film. When attached to a telescope, it can perform such feats as seeing the Moon through thick cloud because it is highly sensitive to the infra-red end of the spectrum. Red light penetrates much more than white light, but not to the human eye. The CCD can thus see objects invisible to ordinary telescopes.

Machines containing CCDs of a kind originally built to scan the night sky for stars, galaxies and quasars are about to be put in service scanning human breasts. Trials will soon begin at Manchester and Edinburgh universities.

As Harvey McGilivray, an astronomer at the Royal Observatory at Edinburgh, recently put it: 'The technique of scanning the night sky for faint objects and scanning the human breast for deposits of calcium, the precursors of tumours, are virtually the same. All you are doing is looking for white objects against a black background. In scanning for tumours you are looking for dark objects against a white background.'

One of the most uncomfortable medical tests a woman can undergo is a breast biopsy, in which a scalpel is used to extract flesh for cancer tests. Using a CCD chip made to give the Hubble space telescope sharper images of distant galaxies, a needle replaces the scalpel. It extracts a tiny sample from the suspect area which the chip examines from two angles. 'The patient can go dancing the same night instead of being exhausted from surgery,' said Ann Jenkins, of NASA's Goddard Space Flight Centre in Baltimore.

CCDs will soon turn up in dentists' surgeries, replacing the X-ray camera and accompanying technician along with increasingly onerous regulations. No longer will the patient have to fear over-exposure to radiation.

Russian cosmonauts landing from the Mir space station on the steppes of Kazakhstan must stagger about in a 'penguin suit' with elastic cords to exercise the muscles to alleviate the crippling effects of weight after living in zero gravity. Now, according to *Aerospace Daily*, under an agreement between the US and Russia, similar penguin suits are being designed for children with walking disorders.

Reverse thrusters slow down the Boeing 777, the world's most advanced airliner, by means of an ultra super-light-weight device in its engines. This is made from graphite epoxy, the same material that was used for the containers that carried British Aerospace's solar power panels up to the Hubble telescope to give it electricity during the repair mission by the astronauts in 1993.

The same material is being used to make new kinds of antennae in broadcasting satellites that could aim television broadcasts at widely separated cities on Earth, eliminating much of the need for cable.

And sensors made for Hubble's cameras are being designed to test the insulation on high-voltage power lines. Electrical leakage costs billions of pounds every year.

But why, some people will ask, could not these marvellous devices have been designed directly for use on this planet without first employing them in space? The answer lies in human nature. Without the compulsive demands of space technology, we might never have got round to building them.

A Car the Size of a Rice Grain

S cene is a battle field of the future. The troops await combat. Suddenly the 'enemy' appears from over the horizon in the form of a thin, rapidly advancing cloud. It consists of omnivorous locusts which with equal enthusiasm eat crops, gun metal, rubber, clothing and even human flesh.

Yet these locusts are not living creatures. They are self-replicating engines, incredibly tiny but vastly sophisticated. Such devices are seen as one of the many future applications of the growing science of 'nanotechnology' – building extremely small machines. Based on the Greek word 'nano', meaning dwarf, the word is a measurement that has come to mean a thousandth of a millionth a metre and promises to transform the world in the next century even more profoundly than computers, aircraft and satellites have transformed ours.

In a recent real-life scene, scientists eagerly watched the screen of a super-computer at the Nippon Telegraph and Telephone Corporation in Tokyo. It slowly filled up with images of coloured, spherical objects in three dimensions.

They looked like a row of Easter eggs. In reality they were atoms of the metallic element molybdenum that is used for hardening and strengthening steel. 'For the first time we can watch atomic events in the real world, and dream of using them to build tiny machines,' said one of the watchers, Dr Reizo Kaneko.

It has taken 2,400 years, since Democritus first proposed the existence of atoms, for us to see them.

The first step in this direction was the electron micro-scope, which obtained its resolution by shining a beam of electrons, rather than one of light, on an object. The latest such device is far more powerful. Known as the 'scanning probe microscope', it physically senses a surface rather than magnifying it. With this, scientists can create three-dimensional images of its atomic structure. They can even pick up its individual atoms and move them.

To demonstrate the power of nanotechnology, Japanese scientists recently built the world's smallest car. It was the size of a grain of rice and weighed about a thousandth of an ounce. It was less than two thirds of a centimetre long and came complete with wheels, headlights, bumpers and a spare tire.

Colin Humphreys, a materials scientist at Cambridge University, said: 'Silicon, of which computer chips are made, is normally opaque. But at the nanometre scale it emits light. With nanometre-sized chips you could therefore build a computer that transmitted its internal signals at the speed of light. Since signals inside a conventional computer travel at only at about a twentieth of this speed, the super-miniaturization that reduced distances inside the machine, together with light-emitting silicon, could produce computers hundreds of millions of times faster than today's.'

Medicine and dentistry promise the most spectacular advances. Jurgen Mohr, of the Karlsruhe Nuclear Research Centre in Germany, said: 'Imagine a dentist of the future who was removing plaque from your teeth. He would not need to do any scraping with metal tools. Instead, he could squirt in a spray of nano machines that would remove all the plaque within seconds. Other tiny machines could also remove heart-threatening cholesterol from human arteries.'

Humphreys added: 'The problem of replacing the body's organs may soon be solved. We have discovered in the last

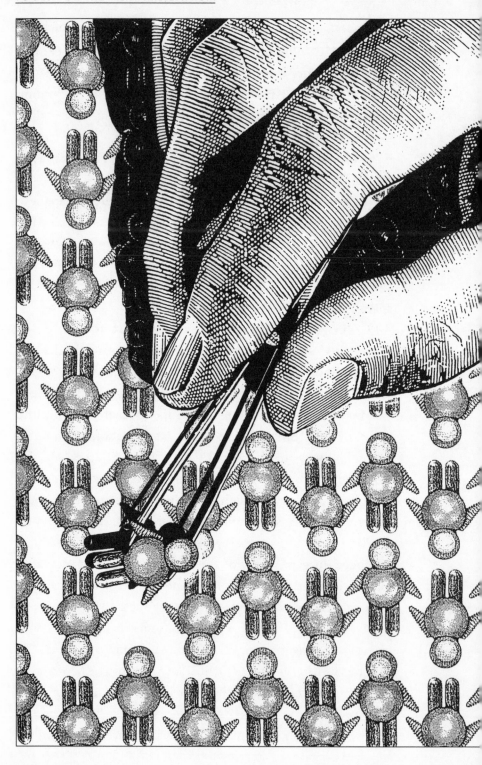

few months that, on a nanometre scale, one piece of bone can be grafted on to another. We should therefore be able to make artificial bones, and grow them on to existing ones, without fear of rejection.'

When some of these advances will actually happen is of course unclear, but many researchers expect many of them will be in place by 2010. K. Eric Drexler, whose 1986 book, *The Engines of Creation*, started popular interest in very small machines, believes that nanotechnology will ultimately be able to do anything that is not forbidden by natural laws (such as turning iron into gold, going faster than light, and building perpetual motion machines). Most significantly, it will enable huge numbers of people to have the finest foods and the most luxurious clothing without being accused of depriving anyone else of them.

But the history of military technology suggests that there will inevitably be a dark side. Omnivorous artificial locusts may be the least of what we have to fear from the next century's dictators.

The Curse of Sleep

For nearly two million years, or about 100,000 human generations, our ancestors spent their nights in caves to be safe from wild beasts. Human brains became addicted to nocturnal slumber and now, with millions of workers around the world doing night shifts, their sleepiness costs about £250 billion a year in accidents, lost productivity and health care.

Martin Moore-Ede of Harvard Medical School, one of the world's foremost experts on sleep and the author of an article in *New Scientist*, says: 'Since the invention of electric light, which made it possible to work at night, we have been a twenty-four-hour society and we are not fitted for it.

'During those millions of years, our brains developed a tiny cluster of cells called the suprachiasmic nucleus, which induces semi-hibernation for about eight hours in every twenty-four. This legacy can cause workers on night shifts to be drowsy when they ought to be alert. It has resulted in horrendous accidents, all of which occurred in the early hours of the morning.'

In recent years these have included:

• The Chernobyl nuclear disaster in 1986, which killed hundreds and exposed millions more to abnormal radiation. It was caused at 1.23 a.m., when a foreman tried to shut down the reactor by the wrong method.

• The Challenger space shuttle explosion in the same year, which killed seven astronauts and halted the US space programme for three years. The shuttle was launched in very bad weather by managers who had not slept for 20 hours.

• In 1988, the Clapham Junction rail disaster, which killed 35 people, happened because a traffic signal had been incorrectly wired by a technician who had had only one day off in 13 weeks.

• The blunders at Three Mile Island in 1979, which have crippled America's nuclear power industry, and cost £700 million to clean up, were made at 4 a.m.

• The Bhopal chemical leak in 1984, the worst industrial catastrophe in history, killing 2,500, occurred in the early hours of the morning.

• The navigational error of the Exxon Valdez tanker in 1989, which polluted 1,200 miles of Alaskan coastline, costing Exxon £2 billion so far with £50 billion in pending damage claims, was made in the middle of the night and blamed on crew fatigue.

It is estimated that about 50 per cent of motorway deaths in America are caused by drivers falling asleep. 'Drowsiness at the wheel is just as great a problem as drunken driving, and yet it receives far less attention,' says Moore-Ede.

'Many engineers and managers do not understand the problem. They are still striving to build more comfort into the flight decks of planes, train cabs, lorries and control rooms in the mistaken belief that comfort improves workers' performance. But this can be a mistake. To be fully alert, one has to be a little uncomfortable, especially in the small hours of the night.'

As founder of the consultancy Circadian Technologies, Moore-Ede recommends 'keep awake' devices such as playing radios, wafting smells and shining bright lights. 'In a nocturnal environment, which can consist of hours of bore-dom punctuated by moments of terror, it can be very dangerous to have only silence and dimmed lights.'

Where may sleep-induced tragedy occur next? Moore-Ede sees the Scottish offshore oil industry as a danger point. Amid tense competition, contractors have mounted a campaign to gain exemption from EU legislation to restrict night work. There are round-the-clock shifts, some of them as long as 15 hours, with intense pressure to cut costs, which can mean fewer people working longer.

But the industry seems less than aware of the danger. 'We do not discuss staff relations with the press,' an offshore oil company spokesman said.

The Daily Me

I t is a Sunday a few years from now. Police Inspector Jones and his wife sit at the breakfast table and read their copies of the *Sunday Telegraph* – but their two front pages bear no resemblance to each other.

The articles on Mr Jones's are all about crime: an arrest that he himself made the day before, a jewel robbery that took place at 5 a.m., and a gun battle that occurred still later. Turning to the Comment pages, he finds an acrimonious debate between two fingerprint experts.

His wife finds not a word about crime in her paper. It is all about gardening. Article after article enthuses about lawns and flowerbeds. Unexpectedly, page three is entirely devoted to Japanese cooking – because the newspaper's computer has noticed her interest in this subject from her past reading.

Welcome to the Newspaper of the Future, which contains only the kind of news that you want to read; what Nicholas Negroponte, head of the Massachusetts Institute of Technology's Media Lab, calls *The Daily Me*. It is never delayed by lie-a-bed paper delivery boys or broken-down vans. It can be read 24 hours a day and is updated every few minutes. It is wholly electronic and its contents come to our homes down the telephone lines from editorial offices.

The biggest revolution in media technology since newspapers replaced town-criers in the eighteenth century may be with us within four years. (It has already begun with such round-the-clock news services as Ceefax, Compuserve and the *Electronic Telegraph*.) It comes with the ever growing power of the silicon chip and the realization by publishers that there is nothing meritorious about spending billions of pounds a year cutting down trees.

The last big newspaper printing plant has probably already been built. 'Publishers are in the business of selling information, not newspapers,' says the consultant Nora Ariel. 'People buy the content, not the wrapper. Newspaper owners are at risk if they fail to understand that they are in the information business, just as railways suffered by thinking that they could stick with trains, not realizing that they were in the transport industry.'

Peter Kruger, of the UK-based Digithurst electronic consultancy, says: 'If newspapers didn't already exist, they wouldn't stand a chance of getting off the drawing board in a world where communication is mostly electronic and increasingly digital.'

So what domestic machines will consumers need to receive newspapers of the future? Nobody is quite sure, and most Western newspaper groups are spending huge sums trying to find out. 'One problem is that most schemes now being discussed require consumers to have more money than they actually have,' says Kruger.

Household television sets would do the job admirably but most of them are too bulky to be carried on trains or read in parks. The most likely gadgets are 'Personal Digital Assistant', hand-held personal computers. If they doubled up as fax machines, diaries, calendars and notebooks, they could justify themselves to most households at a price of about £300.

Just as newspapers have changed the people who read them, electronic delivery will have vast cultural and psychological effects. 'Access to any detail of the news exactly when we want it, with the ability to call up any background details, will vastly increase our understanding of other people,' says Kruger. 'It may be that, in the future, communities split by bigotry and hatred, like Bosnia and Northern Ireland, will disappear because people will have the means to understand each other better.'

Whatever gadgetry they use, Inspector Jones and his wife will leave the breakfast table formidably expert in their kind of reading – crime and gardening.

When Dense Prose Fogs the Issue

I hate long arguments, verbosely expressed.

William Cowper

Computers and word processors have proved invaluable editing tools for writers. But, until now, they have been unable to perform the highest function of an editor, that of helping us to write better English. A new computer program called PARSE changes all that.*

It will be a useful analytical tool for people who write badly but cannot see anything wrong with their prose. Their subject matter may be interesting and important, their facts accurate, their spelling correct and their sentences grammatical – but still, to their bewilderment and fury, the only effect on readers is to send them to sleep.

Boring prose issues in torrents from academics, civil servants, public relations firms, lawyers and scientists. Reading such prose can provoke the sensation of being engulfed in 'fog'. Long sentences have to be read twice because, having reached the end of them, one cannot remember how they began.

The same can apply if there are too many words of three or more syllables. The grammarian Robert Gunning, in his

---

*It is only fair to add that, since this was written, PARSE-like programs have been incorporated into the best modern word processors. But few of them are anything like as good as PARSE. And the fact that software designers saw the need for them is extremely interesting.

1952 book *The Technique of Clear Writing*, published an equation to calculate the 'Fog Index' – the degree of boringness – in a given document. PARSE performs that computation automatically.

The Gunning equation divides the number of words in the document by the number of sentences. It then adds to this the number of words which have three or more syllables, and multiplies by 0.4. This figure is the document's Fog Index. As a rule of thumb, an Index of between 3 and 11 is good prose, one between 12 and 14 is long-winded, while anything above 15 is tending towards intolerably verbose, verging on legalese.

I tested PARSE on three documents of widely differing literary styles: a passage from Karl Marx's *Das Kapital*, a chapter from *Alice in Wonderland* and Earnest Hemingway's classically terse gangster story *The Killers*.

Within seconds, my computer gave its verdict on Karl Marx: a passage of 450 words contained no less than 96 words that had 3 or more syllables, and the whole passage contained only 23 sentences. With an average of 19.6 words per sentence, this yielded a shatteringly unreadable Fog Index of 16.3.

The first few pages from the Mad Hatter's tea-party in *Alice* fared much better. The Fog Index was down to 10.7. Hemingway's short story consisted mostly of passages such as: 'Shut up,' said Al. 'You talk too goddam much.' It yielded a Fog Index of 5.5, indicating a style that may even be a little too terse and staccato for some readers.

Pixelating Her Majesty

The Queen and the late Fred Astaire never danced together. So I had a picture of them created doing just that – showing how new image-processing computer software can not only fake photographs, but make the fraud undetectable.*

An expensive business it is not. A personal computer and the appropriate software, costing about £200, is all that is needed.

So how is it done? In the old days, a picture could be altered by deleting one image and, if necessary, pasting in a new one. In digital imaging – a process first invented merely

---

*We, being amateurs, our forgery was very far from being undetectable. The CIA's former chief photo analyst for forgeries, Dino A. Brugioni, has this to say of it:

'While the picture displays good proportion and composition, it was relatively easy to determine that it was faked. The sources of light on the Queen and Astaire are clearly different. The source for Astaire is a soft one, probably stage lighting, and comes from above and to the left. The source for the Queen, on the other hand, comes from her side and slightly to the right. The intensity of this light, especially on her face, elbow and gown, indicated a flash source at her height and at a fairly close range.

'Note the light on the crown of Astaire's head. The light on his brow is casting a shadow on his eye socket, and his nose is casting a shadow on his lips and chin. His jaw is clearly outlined and his neck is in shadow. To conform to Astaire's light source, the crown of the Queen's hair would have been highlighted, her cheek darkened rather than highlighted, her jaw outlined as clearly as Astaire's, and her neck in the same dark shadow as Astaire's.

'There is something fraudulent about the shadow to the left of Astaire's shoe. It is not consistent with the contour of the shoe or the shadow being cast by its tip. The Queen's neck would not be casting a shadow on her stole, and the top of her stole would have been highlighted rather than in shadow.

'I note also that the Queen's left hand is gloved but that her right hand on Astaire's shoulder is not. If I hadn't known that this was Astaire's dancer's hand I should easily have deduced this because the fingers on the gloved hand are larger than those without. And I am sure that the Queen would have enjoyed immensely dancing with Mr Astaire, and there would have been a smile of pure joy on her face.'

to 'enhance' photographs – the picture is treated in the same way as a word processor treats a document. But instead of words it manipulates the 'pixels', the millions of tiny dots which make up the picture.

With a computer equipped with a CD-ROM drive which can hold gigantic quantities of data as well as huge collections of pictures, the owner has a pictorial database of almost unlimited power. Photographs can be merged with each other just as easily as the text of two or more word-processed documents.

Manipulating with colour is more difficult than with black and white – but not much. The colours of the pixels, which might originally have been blue, red or yellow, can be changed, moved to another part of the picture or scrapped altogether.

Moving film is not immune from alteration. The film of Michael Crichton's novel, *Rising Sun* – in which a piece of film is doctored to falsify evidence of murder – has already shown the possibilities. This can only work if the film is digitally stored and not on tape. But plans to digitize up to 50,000 films – all the films ever made in the Western world – may provide temptations.

Rodger Tamblyn, who created our Fred Astaire picture, says: 'It needed a lot of patience. I merged two pictures of Astaire and the Queen. I removed the girl he was dancing with and replaced her with the Queen.

'But since the Queen's feet were not showing, I gave her the original girl's right foot. Then I tilted the Queen backwards a bit so that she looks up into Astaire's face. Finally I put the girl's hand on Astaire's shoulder, and made sure the shadows from the two original pictures matched.'

'Pictures like this can seem dependable evidence of what did not take place,' said William Mitchell, of the Massachusetts Institute of Technology, author of an article in *Scientific American*. To prove it, Mitchell produced pictures of Marilyn Monroe with her arm around Abraham Lincoln, and President Bush giving Margaret Thatcher a lecherous kiss in the White House garden.

The *New Scientist* has shown a highly convincing forged picture of John Major chatting with Einstein on the steps of Number 10. It is easy to fool people who want to be fooled. Sherlock Holmes's creator Arthur Conan Doyle believed passionately in fairies. Someone obligingly photographed some young girls and superimposed them on a flower. Conan Doyle insisted they were fairies.

In 1986, an anti-nuclear group sent the CBS TV network a picture purporting to show that the Chernobyl disaster was even worse than it was. CBS told Dino Brugioni, retired resident picture analyst at the CIA, that they were about to air the picture as proof that two reactors had melted down. 'Only an idiot would make such a statement,' said Brugioni, who recognized that the background was not of Chernobyl at all. CBS nonetheless went ahead and made the broadcast.

Mr Brugioni once spotted a 'double' of Mao Tse-tung by the shape of the man's ear, since ears are as distinctive as fingerprints. 'While this new technology can be beneficial – in identifying missing children who have aged, for example – it can also be very dangerous,' he said. 'It is a new way of inflicting harm.

'People are sceptical about the authenticity of written documents, but they find it difficult to believe that a picture can be false. With an outdoor picture I can tell you the exact date and time of day it was taken by the angle of the shadows. If the foliage doesn't match the data, then the picture's a fake.

'You can also tell whether the picture is probable. When Marilyn Monroe links arms with Lincoln, the President ought to look more excited at the attention of so beautiful a girl.'

Energy Without Limit

One of the most fascinating conjectures about future space technology, which attracted less attention than it deserved when aired at the 1994 meeting of the British Association for the Advancement of Science, was that our descendants might put in orbit a mini black hole to attract limitless energy from it.

Proposed by Ian Fells, professor of energy conservation at Newcastle University, the idea was that gaseous matter, streaming towards the hole on its way to being devoured, would be travelling at such speed that it could be made to drive turbines.

'It may sound far-fetched, but 200 years ago the idea of harnessing the electric force that makes lightning to produce electricity sounded equally far-fetched,' said Fells, acknowledging that he had not made any attempt to work out the practical details.

The idea was given further respectability by the Astronomer Royal, Sir Martin Rees, who told the meeting that such a black hole, to be useful and safe, would have the weight of a large mountain but would be compressed by its own gravity until it was smaller than an atom.

The project's obvious difficulties only make it seem more interesting. The energy would indeed be limitless, since the hole would never get any smaller. But it might prove very difficult to construct. Black holes – collapsed matter with so strong a gravitational field that nothing, not even light, can escape from them – could perhaps be created by compressing the iron that is found in galactic dust. I did some of the calculations when writing my 1977 book *The Iron Sun: Crossing the Universe through Black Holes*, and they seemed to be workable.

But my calculations applied only to black holes of several stellar masses. Mini black holes, according to cosmological theory, were created by the violent convulsions of the early universe, and it is by no means certain that we could reproduce such conditons. Moreover, Stephen Hawking has predicted that black holes do not remain permanently 'black'. They explode with unimaginable violence (although according to his mathematics this would occur long after the Solar System had disappeared).

There would be two other advantages to the scheme. It would not only provide energy; it would also, being a black hole, give us infinite facilities for garbage disposal. And it could resist attempts by environmentalists to halt it; for once construction of the hole had begun – such is the nature of gravity – it would be physically impossible to halt.

Fells, appropriately, has a healthy contempt for mindless environmental oppositon to energy projects. 'We could still build an 8,000-megawatt reactor, adding six per cent to Britain's energy production, from the tidal energies of the Severn estuary. Environmentalists oppose this on the grounds that it would somehow be disadvantageous to wading birds. But the birds would be perfectly happy to wade somewhere else.'

The Odeon in your Living-room

As our television screens get larger, resolution and sound-effects better and video recorders 'smarter', the disappearance both of cinemas and the television broadcasting industry looms ever closer. Christmas just won't be the same . . .

Movie-watching at home with a rented video will have all the pleasures of a visit to the cinema, but with none of

the inconveniences – like having to queue for entry in the rain, often to be told that all seats are taken, and then walking on sticky floors to expensive and uncomfortable seats where eating, drinking, smoking and talking are forbidden.

A growing number of Americans are spending thousands of dollars setting up the appropriate equipment at home – and a tour of what is available in high-tech British shops like those in London's Tottenham Court Road reveals that many Britons are doing the same.

The only obstacle, according to an article in the latest *Fortune*, is what the magazine calls WAF – the 'Wife Acceptance Factor'. Assembling large amounts of electronic apparatus with dozens of dials and switches, preferably

brightly coloured, is a pastime that appeals mostly to males. If the wife is not consulted beforehand 'she may be understandably reluctant to have the living-room made to resemble the control room of the starship *Enterprise*.' But, assuming it can be done without divorce, the practical details are straightforward.

The first important step is to install a large-enough TV screen. A metre is about the minimum to ensure cinema-like realism. Next, put in several speakers. The average home TV has only one, making reception far inferior to that in a cinema. Since it is sensible to build incrementally, and not try to achieve perfection at once with all the inevitable bugs, the next step is to increase the number of speakers still further, with one central one and several subsidiary ones to each side. This will ensure that, wherever you are sitting, sounds appear to come from sources that you see on the screen, and that the room has no 'cheap seats'.

This can best be done by installing a Dolby 'surround sound' with decoding circuitry. It will give the illusion that one is actually in the place depicted in the film. In *Jurassic Park*, for example, one would be able to hear the central thump of the footsteps of Tyrannosaurus Rex in the foreground as well as the lesser background sounds made by the wind and the cicadas.

The right equipment must be bought with great care. Many experts believe the purchases involved in each step should take several days. Bjorn Dybdahl, owner of Bjorn's Audio Video shop in San Antonio, Texas, said: 'If you walk into a shop and say you're interested in home theatre, and the salesman says: "I have one you can buy right over here," turn around and walk out.'

However, films with stories written in their entirety by someone else may soon be antiquated. Connect a personal computer to the apparatus, with future 'artificial intelligence' software, and it will be possible to see a film whose plot unfolds differently because the person watching it becomes one of the characters. Even sex with imaginary lovers becomes possible. We will enter another world and mould its destiny.

This process can be taken still further with coming generations of computer games where the on-screen graphics will be as lifelike as at the cinema. This could ultimately create illusions like those in Arthur C. Clarke's 1961 novel *The City and the Stars*, where people take part in fantastic adventures in ways that are indistinguishable from reality.

These technologies will obviously bring great social change. When they have become as cheaply available as colour television was a decade ago, publicly scheduled television will largely vanish.

Forget the ceaseless interviews with politicians, forget the feeble 'chat shows' that people only look at because they have nothing else to watch, and forget the expensive commercials that companies only pay for because audiences are sufficiently large. When the number of watchers starts to shrink towards zero, an entire industry will quietly disappear. As for the effects on society itself, they will surely be incalculable.

Heavenly Computers

Designers of computers of the future have found inspiration in a most unlikely source – the theological Doctrine of the Holy Trinity.

The doctrine states that there are three 'Persons' in the one God: the Father, the Son and the Holy Ghost, absolutely co-equal in authority. It was agreed on by nearly all the major philosophers of the Middle Ages, but it sounds alien to modern unbelievers more used to hierarchical chains of command.

According to the Creed of St Athanasius in the fourth century, supported later by St Augustine of Hippo, St Thomas Aquinas and, in Ireland, St Patrick with his shamrock: 'In the Trinity none is afore or after; none is greater or less than another; but the whole three Persons are co-eternal together; and co-equal.'

In a hierarchical system, the sergeant takes orders from the colonel, and the colonel from the general. Computers as we know them are ruled by a single chip, the so-called 'central processing unit', which commands all the others. However, computer scientists are looking at new ways of rearranging the command chain, using a horizontal model taken from the Three Persons Doctrine.

William McLaughlin, an astrophysicist at the Jet Propulsion Laboratory at Pasadena, California, said: 'The doctrine represents a revolutionary form of logic which is ideal for new forms of computer systems.' Writing in *Spaceflight*, the monthly journal of the British Interplanetary Society, he suggests that computer scientists who study St

Augustine's *De Trinitate* will find a way to build machines that can make decisions intuitively, like humans, rather than with the coldly formal – and often infuriatingly stupid – logic we now associate with computers.

Instead of having just one master control-chip, a Trinity computer would have three. Each would be an independent entity, acting as the head of an independent command structure comprising three subsidiary chips. This would make a total of nine, a number that some management studies have concluded is ideal for taking the decisions in an organization. All decisions by the computer would be a result of a 'vote' among the ruling three.

In human affairs, horizontal – or trinitarian – authority has not always been a success. The Roman Republic was twice ruled by triumvirates, and on each occasion the paranoid jealousies of the three rulers led to civil war. Computer chips, however, do not try to destroy each other; they only decide 'yes', or 'no'. The British computer expert Julian Allason said: 'A Trinity computer might be able to do things without being told how to do them. This will be a vital component of what we expect in future machine "intelligence".

'In processing huge amounts of data, it would be able to see patterns that are often invisible to conventional machines. It would thus be able to think "intuitively", mimicking some of the almost infinitely different ways in which people think.

'They would be adept at lateral thinking, otherwise known as fuzzy logic, where the solution to a problem lies outside the system being studied. No conventional computer, for example, would ever suggest that an adult illness might have been caused by a childhood vaccination.'

Modern religious philosophers may look at trinitarian computers with an indulgent eye. Father Anthony Meredith, a Jesuit theologian, said: 'As far as logic is concerned,

McLaughlin is perfectly right. The Three Persons, although equal in authority, have different roles. As defined by St Augustine of Hippo in the fifth century, the Father is the creator, the Son the redeemer, and the Holy Ghost the sanctifier.'

The medieval philosophers have had a bad press. Macaulay said they 'filled the world with long beards and long words and left it as ignorant as they found it'. But an epoch of new logic demands a second look at old logic. It will be a courageous manufacturer who changes from the single master-chip computer architecture invented by John von Neumann in the 1940s. Many will insist on staying with the equivalent of the Sabellian Heresy.

The Libyan bishop Sabellius rejected the Trinity, believing the Father alone had authority. Modern Sabellians will have to be overthrown as their forefathers were seventeen centuries ago.

Cars without Drivers

I n a film version of H.G. Wells's novel *The Invisible Man*, a traffic policeman stops a car that is being driven above the speed limit. To his astonishment and horror, there is no driver at the wheel.

This situation has occurred in real life – without the policeman – when a Pontiac mini-van made one of the most remarkable journeys since the invention of the motor car. It travelled 400 kilometres by motorway from Pittsburgh to Washington, at an average speed of 92 kilometres per hour, without a human driver.

The van was almost entirely driven by a computer and attached robots, with a human supervisor – Dean Pomerleau of the Robotics Institute at Carnegie Mellon University in Pittsburgh – sitting beside the steering wheel but seldom touching it. He called the experience 'hands-off, feet-off, brains-off driving'. His supervision made the experiment so safe that he did not need to warn the police.

A forward-pointing video camera mounted just below the rearview mirror 'read' the road in front of the van, taking in such information as the positions of other vehicles, lane markings and distances to the kerb and to the motorway's central barrier. It sent this data to a laptop computer sitting between the two front seats. The computer processed the data and continually instructed an electric motor to move the steering wheel left or right. Electric power for the entire system came from the van's cigarette lighter.

To make things still more interesting, the last 24 kilometres of the journey were not on the comparatively predictable motorway but on a minor road, the George Washington Parkway, which has many curves, overhanging trees and other features liable to 'confuse' the machine.

The system has several bad habits which have not yet been cured. It does not recognize red lights and will drive straight through them if not stopped. It cannot tell the difference between sunlight and the headlights of an oncoming car. It cannot change lanes by itself and sometimes, for some inexplicable reason, it turns into exit roads without being told to do so.

Driverless cars, although in their infancy, promise a vast reduction in the number of accidents within a few decades. Since almost all accidents are caused by drivers, the ideal solution is to abolish them.

There is a precedent for such optimism in the chess-playing machines that routinely defeat all but a handful of grandmasters. Road conditions, for all their possible variations, are considerably less complicated than positions on a chessboard. A chess machine is programmed to remember a huge number of positions, knowing from past experience how to react to them. It seems overwhelmingly probable that the hitherto baffling problems of road safety can be solved in the same way.

An electronic driver, like a chess machine, would remember past 'positions'. Confronted by a patch of oil on the road, a drunk lurching in front of the car or a bouncing ball indicating the presence of playing children, it would know how to react.

'But cars that drive themselves so safely that you can tell them your desired destination and go to sleep are still at least ten years away,' says Pomerleau. 'One great electronic improvement which should prevent a lot of accidents could, however, be ready in as little as three years. This is a warning system that wakes drivers up when they start to fall asleep.'

About half the motorway deaths in the Western world are caused by drivers falling asleep at the wheel. It is a problem as serious as drunken driving. A gadget operated by electrodes planted in the driver's skull that would beep if he showed signs of drowsiness would be a tremendous step towards death-free roads.

In a short story Isaac Asimov half-jokingly suggested that a major problem of the future might be the wild social life of intelligent cars. They would go out by themselves to parties where they would 'mate' and produce young. While this may never happen, we can visualize situations in which they are independent beings as seemingly intelligent as chauffeurs and immeasurably faster in making decisions.

'I'll Be Back!'

Robots like the Terminator, programmed to hunt and kill particular people, could be feasible within a few years. They may not look quite like Arnold Schwarzenegger in the cult films but they could be just as deadly.

'Already it is technically possible to build a robot that would roam about and kill everyone it met who had blonde hair,' said Kevin Warwick, head of Reading University's cybernetics department, who lectured to a packed hall on the darker side of machine 'intelligence' of the future.

'It has been argued by some scientists, notably Roger Penrose in his 1989 book *The Emperor's New Mind*, that such machines are theoretically impossible because they could not be made aware of their own existence.

'But I believe that view is wrong and that such books are less than responsible. To act with intelligence, a machine does not need self-awareness. It only needs a purpose,' says Warwick. 'A good example of a machine with such a purpose is a chess-playing computer. It can even defeat its own creator. It has the overriding goal to win the game, yet it does not even know it is playing a game.'

Warwick and his colleagues have built a team of miniature robots with insect-like intelligence which he calls the Seven Dwarfs. Each has a computer chip for a 'brain' and 'sees' with ultrasonic eyes. They can be programmed either to hunt each other or to flee from each other across his laboratory floor.

'In a few years' time, to judge by present advances in the speed and memory of computers, it will be possible to build a much larger version of such a robot, for police or military purposes, but which a criminal could programme to seek and assassinate his victims.

'It is essential to understand that computers and robots do not think like we do and, as Penrose has correctly pointed out, probably could not even be programmed to do so. They do not have any in-built capacity for humanity or mercy, and it is idle to think that we can protect ourselves from them by any device like Isaac Asimov's proposed "first law of robotics", which states that a machine must not harm a human being.

'We set the machine a goal, expecting it to execute the goal in our way. But instead, it executes it in its way. A superb example of this was seen in the 1969 film *The Forbin Project*, in which a computer was instructed to take over the world's nuclear weapons with instructions to bring about "peace". But it achieved peace by massacring nearly everyone.'

Meanwhile, experimenters at the Information Research Laboratories in Kyoto, Japan, are trying to build a robot with the brains of a cat. This does not mean that it will be furry or chase mice or want saucers of milk, but that it will do things without being told how to do them. It will program itself and then execute its own program. It will be the first robot that is more intelligent than an insect. Yet, devoid of morals or common sense, such robotic 'animals' are all too easily liable to behave in ways that are totally at variance with what their builders intended.

Warwick believes that too many people do not appreciate the danger of such misunderstandings. They rely too much on the supposed wisdom of computers, he says. Banks, for example, have machines that decide whether a particular person should be given a loan. But the computer is liable to reason in ways in which its designer never intended.

'For example, it might have twice before rejected loan applications by people who happened to be left-handed. It could then decide, without announcing that it was doing so, to reject all applications from left-handers.' It may be a small step from stupidity to crime.

Reaper and Creeper

Computer scientists from Hebrew University in Jerusalem flew home from a recent conference in Cincinnati to some very unpleasant news. They had been telling their American colleagues of their fears of electronic viruses – malicious software inserted into computers that wipes out files and programs.

On their return they found that such a virus had attacked all the interlinked personal computers in Jerusalem. Fortunately the villain had made two errors – one technical, the other religious.

He or she had left a tell-tale trace of the attempted sabotage, so that when any of the affected computers were switched on, an abnormal message flashed briefly on the screens, indicating that there had been some tampering with the programs.

The virus was due to activate on Saturday, Israel's Sabbath, a day when few people would be working at their terminals. There was plenty of time to warn them through the newspapers. A plot that might have done significant damage to Israel's economy had been foiled by the incompetence of its perpetrator.

Computer viruses are quite different from hacking – the malicious art of computer snooping. The viruses are maliciously designed to do the maximum damage to a computer system by destroying all the software.

In many ways they work exactly like their biological counterparts. A virus may attach itself to a program or a file in such a way (unlike the effort of the Jerusalem saboteur) that it cannot be detected. It can then make a copy of itself which it transfers to the next piece of software before destroying its original host. It continues this process until everything in the computer's memory disks has been wiped out.

Another kind of virus does the opposite. Instead of destroying everything in memory, or in the memory storage disks, it gradually fills up all the free space with garbage, so that eventually the computer cannot be used.

In one example a programmer feeling aggrieved after being sacked from a large company left a 'gift' behind him in the company's computer. It was a tiny program called Creeper, occupying no more than 400 bytes, that had only one function: to make an exact copy of itself.

Twenty-four hours after the sacked programmer had left, it woke up, duplicated itself and went to sleep again. No harm done yet. A massive computer with a memory of 300 million bytes had merely been invaded by a paltry 800 alien bytes of coding. But two days later the two copies of Creeper again procreated. Now there were four of them, totalling 1,600 bytes. So the process went on, day after day . . . 8, 16, 32 copies of Creeper, remorselessly eating up memory space. And still nobody noticed they were there.

At the end of a fortnight strange things started to happen to some of the peripheral functions of the company's computer. There were odd delays and apparent mistakes. For its memory now contained 16,384 identical copies of Creeper – more than 6.5 million bytes of utter rubbish.

After 20 days the computer refused to perform any task whatsoever. Its memory was overwhelmed by the presence of more than half a million copies of Creeper.

In desperation the company created emergency memory space into which they introduced a program of their own called Reaper. The task of Reaper was to hunt down all copies of Creeper and destroy them.

The war between Reaper and Creeper was like that between Hercules and the Hydra. No sooner had copies of Creeper been destroyed than more appeared. The battle between the two warring programs – in which Reaper was eventually victorious – prevented the computer from carrying out its normal tasks and very nearly bankrupted the company.

But at least the struggle has led to the creation of a new kind of computer game, Core Wars, in which two opposing programs struggle to destroy each other. They even fire at each other with a form of electronic artillery.

Electronic 'vaccines' have been invented to combat viruses. One such product is Safeguard, being sold by the London firm Prosoft. 'Safeguard will check a legitimate program to make sure that no alterations have been made to it since it was last run,' says its manager Robert Mathias. But even Safeguard won't find new programs that have been maliciously inserted. Only constant vigilance and a suspicious mind will do that.

It is unlikely, of course, that a virus could dwell in legitimately sold software. But too many floppy disks are circulated privately, their recipients not bothering to inquire about their origins. Therein lies the danger. That is why experts liken computer viruses to Aids.

A Cable Car to the Heavens

S harp-eyed people in tropical countries were amazed
one week in 1994 to see a long, thin line extending
across the night sky, shining faintly in reflected
sunlight.

This was no UFO but an orbiting man-made 'tether',
20 kilometres long and only an eighth of a centimetre
thick. It was made in the garage of Joe Carroll, founder of
a small Californian group of space enthusiasts called
Tether Applications, and launched into space by hitching a
ride on an unmanned Delta rocket, a feat that astronauts
in space shuttles had been attempting for nearly a year
with much less success.

Carroll's tether consists of a form of polyethylene, the
tough plastic of supermarket shopping bags. Scientists are
watching his experiment, which could have profound consequences for industry in the twenty-first century.

For many years there has been a growing realization that
space technology will be cheaper and more efficient if the
work of rockets is supplemented by other devices. A space
tether could perform a vast number of tasks, from providing
electricity to spacecraft and throwing cargo between the
Earth and the Moon, to ensuring the good health of people
on their way to Mars.

In its simplest form, a tether could be a mini power
station in space. A tether made of semi-conducting material
with one end passing through the Earth's magnetic field
could carry electricity to a spacecraft, supplementing the

work of solar panels which normally power such a craft by direct sunlight.*

'A tether could also heighten or lower the orbit of a spacecraft,' said Carroll. 'Extending from a spacecraft in low Earth orbit, it always wants to point downwards, towards the atmosphere. When its downward end enters the atmosphere, it will be affected by drag, slowing the craft and pulling it downwards.

'Conversely, if the same tether is suddenly cut, pressure will be released and the spacecraft will bound upwards.'

A more ambitious scheme has been proposed by Robert Forward, former chief scientist at the Hughes Research Laboratories, who sees tethers as a future Earth–Moon transport system. 'We hope to "hurl" cargo weighing up to five tons nearly half a million kilometres across space, rather in the way that David used a slingshot to kill Goliath.'

Forward's idea goes like this. Cargo from a space station circling the Earth is to be sent to the Moon without using rockets. The Earth station has a tether extending to the cargo at its end. When the cargo faces the Moon, the tether releases it. The cargo is then caught by another tether attached to a space station orbiting the Moon – like a baseball player catching a ball – and lowered to the lunar surface. 'This system would be ideal for sending to the Moon essential supplies like scarce hydrogen, with which lunar colonists could manufacture water.'

People travelling to Mars would risk ill-health because of the effects of weightlessness. The progressive loss of calcium in their bones can accelerate ageing, and would make them unfit for work on reaching the Red Planet.

---

*In 1996, shuttle astronauts trailed a 20-kilometre tether in the Earth's ionosphere, trying to extract electricity from it. But to everyone's great disappointment the tether snapped, apparently overloaded by the electricity that was moving along it.

The solution would be a rigid tether a few kilometres long. One end would be attached to the Mars ship and the other to a counterbalancing object weighing roughly the same as the ship. By the firing of small rockets, the whole system, ship, tether and counterbalance, would be made to rotate. As on a fairground ride, centrifugal force would create gravity artificially inside the ship, on the side opposite to the tether. By varying rotation speed, gravity of any desired strength could be created on board. A problem would only arise if the ship had to do a mid-course correction.

The most remarkable suggestion of all for a space tether comes from Arthur C. Clarke, who describes what would be a cable car to the heavens. One end of a 36,000-kilometre tether would be attached to a point near the equator and the other to a satellite in geostationary orbit.

A lift would then travel up and down this taut cable, carrying people and freight into high orbit. (The problems and perils of building such a 'cable car to the stars' are graphically described in his novel, *The Fountains of Paradise*.)

A ridiculous notion? 'I predict that it will be built about fifty years after everyone stops laughing,' says Clarke.

And the 1994 experiment? Carroll said: 'My tether was severed in one place by a micrometeorite, but not until it had been in orbit for five days. I count this a success, with this proviso: people using space tethers will always have to allow for occasional breakages.'

The Devil's Digits

Mighty are numbers, joined with art resistless.

Euripides

There may be dangers ahead for those who have put their faith in the mightiness of numbers. A secret code whose security depended on sheer numerical complexity has been found wanting. It appears that once several hundred computers get to work simultaneously, then even the most cunningly hidden mathematical secrets will be revealed.

The widely used RSA cipher (named after its inventors Rivest, Shamir and Adelman), works on the assumption that if two very large prime numbers are multiplied together, it will take centuries – millennia even – for the fastest computer to do the sum *backwards* and identify the two original primes which conceal the secret keys to the cipher.

Take the 'Evil Number' 3,458,137, a discovery of my own. It takes a home computer less than a second to discover why it is 'evil'. After several hundred calculations performed at lightning speed, we find that it is the product of the primes 1789 and 1933, the respective dates of the onset of the French Revolution and of Hitler's rise to power – both thoroughly evil dates.

But if the two prime numbers (divisible only by themselves and one), are not of four digits but more than 100, then, so the three mathematicians reasoned, the problem would be truly 'intractable'. The would-be codebreakers would long have died of old age before they found the hidden figures.

However what they did not reckon with was that 'prime factoring' – as it is called – would become a cult. Looking for hidden primes has become one of the standard tests of a computer's speed. In 1994, a team of mathematicians, using a network of more than 400 computers around the world, succeeded in factoring a number of 129 digits. This spectacular number, known appropriately as RSA 129, was:

114, 381, 625, 757, 888,
867, 669, 235, 779, 976,
146, 612, 010, 218, 296,
721, 242, 362, 562, 561,
842, 935, 706, 935, 245,
733, 897, 830, 597, 123,
563, 958, 705, 058, 989,
075, 147, 599, 290, 026,
879, 543, 541

It was divisible, the 'crackers' announced as their champagne corks popped, by the two primes:

3, 490, 529, 510, 847,
650, 949, 147, 849, 619,
903, 898, 133, 417, 764,
638, 493, 387, 843, 990,
820, 577

and:

32, 769, 132, 993, 266,
709, 549, 961, 988, 190,
834, 461, 413, 177, 642,
967, 992, 942, 539,798,
288, 533.

It was a feat that could have taken a *single* super-computer as much as twenty years.* Euclid started the whole thing more

---

*And, so after all this, how safe is the RSA cipher? The answer is that it is almost certainly safe – for the present – if a prime product of at least 150 digits is used. But this is only true if one is sending messages and files that do not have to remain secret for very long. It is *not* safe for *archival* files, that must preserve their secrecy for many years. Advances in factoring will continue to be made and ever larger numbers will become easy to factor quickly. And yet the whole RSA cipher could be destroyed by the invention of 'quantum computers', when that invention comes.

than 2,000 years ago with his somewhat obscure proof that there is an infinite number of primes. 'Every whole number greater than one,' he then announced portentously, 'is either a prime or it is not. And that shall be called the First Law of Arithmetic.' To which a critic sarcastically replied: 'Every person aged greater than zero is either male or female. And that shall be called the First Law of Humanity.'

Eratosthenes of Cyrene worked out an ingenious 'sieve' to discover all prime numbers up to a given limit. As the rhyme goes:

Strike the twos and strike the threes,
The Sieve of Eratosthenes!
When the multiples sublime,
The numbers that remain are prime.

Prime numbers have since exerted an almost mystic fascination. They appear at random, but many philosophers have refused to believe that this randomness is genuine. Some have held that God arranged them according to a hidden pattern which, if ever discovered, will render man 'divine'.

This prospect alarmed the Church, which feared that only Satan would be malicious enough to make the appearance of primes so unpredictable. 'The danger already exists,' thundered St Augustine, 'that mathematicians have made a covenant with the Devil to darken the spirit and confine man in the bonds of Hell.'

Many people think that the number one ought to be a prime, it being divisible by itself and one, and thus living up to the mathematical definition of a prime. 'But that wouldn't be fair to the other prime numbers,' a mathematician once told me gravely.

Part Four

EDGES OF THE INFINITE

A Sea of Universes

Astronomers are often asked the question: 'What happened before the Big Bang?' Until now this question had a standard, if unsatisfying answer: 'You ask an improper question. Time began with the Big Bang. Asking what happened *before* it, is like asking what is north of the North Pole.'

But this answer will not do any more. It appears that there was a 'before' – not, admittedly, in this universe, but among a vast collection of other universes known as the 'multiverse', of which ours was one of the few to evolve with conditions that favoured life. Many of these parallel universes are likely still to exist, says the cosmologist Michio Kaku, of the City University of New York.

He tells the anecdote of a Russian physicist visiting the roulette tables at Las Vegas who wagers all his money on a single number. 'That's a ridiculous strategy!', his American friends tell him. 'You'll lose it all.' 'Perhaps.' he replies, 'but in at least one parallel universe I'll be rich beyond my wildest imagination.'

The reason for thinking in this way is the realization that Einstein's general theory of relativity, which describes the expansion of the early universe and its coalescence into galaxies, breaks down in the extreme conditions of the Big Bang and must be replaced by quantum cosmology. Temperatures were then 10^{32} degrees, a trillion trillion times hotter than at the centre of an H-bomb explosion, which would have ripped apart all elementary particles except the simplest, the electron.

Now as Heisenberg's uncertainty principle shows us, you cannot ever catch an electron. The more you know of its position, the less you know of its speed, and vice versa.

'The behaviour of the early universe', explains Kaku, 'was identical to that of an electron. It existed in an infinite number of different states simultaneously. Some of these were "favourable", being the seeds of the fundamental constants that we know, while others had something terribly wrong with, for example, the protons decaying after a billion years so that stars would never form.'

Many of these parallel universes must still exist, perhaps like the one in Isaac Asimov's novel *The Gods Themselves* whose inhabitants lacked the hydrogen to form sufficient stars, and so started to steal hydrogen from ours.

And so what of the multiverse that spawned our universe? The simplest analogy, says Kaku, is that of boiling water which continually creates bubbles. From these bubbles universes form.

Can we therefore create a universe in a laboratory? In principle, yes, since the task requires zero energy. Universes are constantly being created in a 'sea of nothing'. But since the heat of the budding universe will be so many trillions of degrees, the experiment might perhaps damage the laboratory.

Scars of Old Collisions

C hesapeake Bay, the site of one of the most famous early English settlements in America, was shaped by the impact of a giant meteorite from space.

The discovery, by an American geology professor, reminds us that the threat of violent destruction by asteroids is ever present – and that there are hundreds of thousands of other craters on the Earth's surface, still undiscovered because they are hidden by vegetation, erosion or the seas.

'The Chesapeake Bay crater is one of the ten biggest meteorite craters on Earth,' says C. Wylie Poag, of the US Geological Survey at Woods Hole, Massachusetts, who made the discovery. In an article in *Geology* called 'Meteorite Mayhem in Ole Virginny', he explains how he discovered in the bay an unusual underground layer of boulders dating back 35 million years.

Using seismic data from oil companies he found a series of concentric rings of which the largest was more than 80 kilometres across and very similar to a smaller underground meteorite crater found recently in Germany.

The finding of these underground rings coincided with the discovery in the region of a layer of 'tektites' – distinctive rocks thrown into the air by a meteorite impact. 'It clearly shows that there is a large impact crater in the southern part of the bay,' says Poag.

Now the plot thickens. The dry, unchanging surface of the Moon is covered with such craters. They range from a few metres across to scores of kilometres in width. It follows therefore that the Earth, whose surface area is 16 times larger than the Moon's, and hence much more likely to attract space debris during the 4.6 billion-year history of the Solar System, must be much more richly covered with them.

But where are they? One at least is clearly visible. Barringer crater in the Arizona desert is nearly two kilometres across and 1,200 metres deep. It marks the place where a rock about 15 metres wide crashed into the ground 20,000 years ago. At the other extreme of violence is the undersea crater recently discovered off the coast of Yucatan, caused by an asteroid as wide as Greater London which struck Earth about 65 million years ago, killing most of the dinosaurs. (See Our Improbable Existence, p. 14.)

It is estimated that there have been at least 2,000 major impacts in the last 600 million years, and many times this number of minor ones. The difficulty facing geologists in the search for them is the huge number of seemingly obvious candidates, many of whose dramatic land formations may only be a coincidence.

Setting aside underground or undersea craters, which are the most difficult to find, there are many places on Earth which, because of the sharpness of their outlines, may be thought to have been gouged out by mighty blows from space.

The Barringer crater is roughly circular, with many sharp angles. Places like this include the Wash, where King John lost his stolen treasure in 1216, the Gulf of Taranto in the heel of Italy, the Gulf of Carpentaria in northern Australia, the Gulf of Mexico, and the immense Hudson Bay in Canada.

Civilization may at least once have been wiped out by a hammer blow from space. This was not Atlantis, the Minoan civilization centred on Crete, with its well-documented destruction in about 1500 BC by vast sea-waves after the volcanic eruption on the nearby island of Santorini, but the empire of the Mycenaeans which dominated the eastern Mediterranean and mysteriously vanished about 1100 BC.

Plato, in his *Timaeus,* tells of Solon, the lawgiver of Athens, who, after a visit to Egyptian scholars, returned to Greece to tell of the terrible fate of what must have been the Mycenaean empire, for it is hard to tell what other empire he could have been referring to. He spoke of destruction caused by 'the bodies that revolve in heaven round the Earth' that brought a 'great conflagration', natural events liable to occur 'at long intervals'.

Scientific proof of such assertions may come by accident, says Poag – with his data from the oil industry – or perhaps even from a treasure hunt.

The value of King John's lost jewels and coin is incalculable. It would be ironic if a search for it, thousands of metres under the Wash, revealed instead tektites or concentric rings that would show that one of England's most famous landmarks was created by an event of almost unimaginable violence.

Check Your Typing!

B udding professional astronomers may have been alarmed by a recent report that there is often a gentle breeze at the La Palma observatory of 'five kilometres per second' – a velocity that would that would surely flatten all the buildings.

Saying 'per second' instead of 'per hour' was typical of the kind of erroneous statement that regularly gets quoted in the 'Here and There' column in *The Observatory*, surely one of the most entertaining regular features in astronomical literature.*

Astronomical writers – like those on any other subject – are liable to make appalling errors. The problem is seldom ignorance – such people are usually very well informed – but carelessness. They too often fail to check what they have written, and either bad grammar, misspelling, use of the wrong term or omitting a crucial word like 'million' or 'billion' renders their words hilarious – like the *New York Times* 1989 announcement that the Galileo mission to Jupiter would cost a mere 1.4 dollars.

Here are some amusing examples from 'Here and There': 'The European solar panels of the Space Telescope will be replaced by astronauts' – *ESA Bulletin*, 1993. 'Clementine is now in low Earth orbit (140 by 160 nanometres)' (a nanometre is a millionth of a metre) – *Lunar and Planetary Information Bulletin*, 1994. And, 'Scotti will use a chronograph to darken the disc of Jupiter' – *Time* magazine, 1994. In a

---

*A journal published by the Royal Astronomical Society.

similar vein, *Nature,* in a splendid misspelling in 1989, told of an astronomer who had 'exploded many stars by computer'.

I myself was once guilty, on the front page of my newspaper, of writing 'miles', when I meant 'light-years', an error with a factor of six trillion. But it is reassuring to note that many professional publications have made similar distance errors.

'The Hubble Space Telescope will enable us to see twelve to fifteen light-years beyond our planet,' said the Astronomy Book Club in 1989. And the *Arizona Summer Wildcat,* a University of Arizona newspaper, reported in 1991 that 'astronomers have found a galaxy six million miles away in Pisces'. ('Something fishy going on' was the `Here and There' comment on this revelation.)

Some errors are so weird that one cannot imagine how they were made. '[The galaxy] NGC4156 does not seem to be associated with NGC4156,' said *Astronomy and Astrophysics* in 1984 and the *Monthly Notices of the Royal Astronomical Society* wrote in 1982 of an object that was 'hotter than itself'.

Sometimes the error is clearly not the author's fault, like the remark in the *New Scientist* in 1990 that the Milky Way has 'roughly 1012 times the mass of the Sun'. The superscript had been omitted, and the number should have been 10^{12}. This is similar to the constantly repeated error, in the days of hot metal typesetting by compositors, of 'cemetery dust' in space.

And for sheer incredibility, nothing can surpass the 1989 advertisement in *Sky and Telescope* for 'Exciting Full-Size Posters of Mercury, Venus, Earth and Mars!' Could they be affecting our climate?

Why We Don't Turn into Werewolves

There is a popular myth, widely held in many parts of the world, in which people are turned into werewolves – or at least behave with violent irrationality – whenever the Moon's tidal forces are strong.

Assuming that this is a gravitational effect, a professor of astrophysics has calculated how large your head would have to be for it to take place – an interesting examination of the oddities of gravity.

'If your brain were, say, 13,000 kilometres in diameter (the size of the Earth), then the Moon's tidal forces would indeed give you an oblong-shaped cranium and induce untold derangements to your mental faculties,' says Neil de Grasse Tyson, of Princeton University, in a series of articles in the American journal *Natural History*.

'For normal Homo sapiens, however, the difference in the Moon's gravity from one side of the head to the other is immeasurably small. The weight of a pillow one is lying on imparts a squeezing force that is more than seven trillion times stronger than the Moon's tidal force, a view not shared by those who write about werewolves.'

For gravitation, although the only one of the four fundamental forces whose effects extend through the universe, is almost immeasurably the weakest. It is normally 10^{36} times (1 followed by 36 noughts) weaker than the next strongest, the electro-magnetic force. But, paradoxically, it can become immeasurably strong, too, in particular beyond the event horizon of a black hole (the remnant of a collapsed star so

massive that nothing, not even light, can escape from it).

The recent discovery of a black hole in a galaxy called M101, 20 million light-years from Earth, that appears to be creating stars rather than devouring them – by hurling out from its orbit streams of hydrogen, the raw material of stars – indicates the future surprises we are likely to encounter from gravity. The most extraordinary of these is the prediction that a corridor circling a black hole could be both straight and curved at the same time. (See A Corridor Both Curved and Straight, p. 229.)

When we stand on the ground, gravity is always slightly stronger – by one ten-thousandth of 1 per cent – at our feet than at our heads. But at the opposite extreme, if we were to fall feet first into a black hole, gravity would become so strong that by accelerating one's feet so much faster than one's head, 'the tidal strength would exceed the strength of the chemical bonds of the flesh, and a human body would be stretched into a long string of falling atoms.'

But weak as 'normal' gravity may be, it is sufficiently strong for the Moon to act as a brake on the Earth's rotation. Days are becoming imperceptibly longer as the oceans, moved by the tides, slow the planet's rotation by friction. A trillion years from now, the rotation will be so slow that an Earth day will equal a lunar month. Since the Sun, as it swells in its dying convulsions, will not be large enough to consume the Earth and Moon, the two bodies will have achieved a solitary 'double tidal lock'. Like Pluto and its moon Charon, one side of each body will permanently face the other.

Gravity can only be created by producing mass, but its effects can be simulated. In a fast-rotating chamber, like the Wall of Death in a fairground, people are pressed against the outside walls by what is unsatisfactorily called 'centrifugal force'. But what is really happening is that they are being made to rotate relative to the mass of the whole universe, according to Einstein.

This observation also explains why astronauts who travel fast enough could return younger than their own children. The friends they left behind would age normally and the accelerated travellers would age more slowly. Why? The travellers move alone, but when the Earth moves the entire universe moves with it.

There is nothing mystical about this prediction. There is no suggestion that the speeding astronauts will turn into werewolves, whatever the gravitational forces.

Coldest of the Cold

The temperature inside the refrigerator in George Pickett's laboratory at Lancaster University is the lowest ever achieved. It is 12 millionths of a degree above absolute zero.

This is about 300,000 times colder than any natural temperature. The empty spaces between the galaxies are almost three degrees above absolute zero, for they are still cooling from the infinite heat of the Big Bang that created our region of the universe some 15,000 million years ago.

Picket and colleagues in the United States are exploring an unknown region where materials behave in extraordinary ways. 'High-energy physicists are historians of the universe,' he explained, 'because they are exploring the infinitely high temperatures and densities of the Big Bang. But we are futurologists, looking at the universe as it will be billions of years hence, when practically all heat has gone.'

Absolute zero is eternally unattainable, according to Hermann Nernst's Third Law of Thermodynamics of 1906, because atoms would be motionless in the total absence of heat, and they are always in motion.

The scale of natural temperatures goes like this:

Where found	Degrees C
The Big Bang	Infinite
Interior of hottest stars	1,000 million
Core of the Sun	30 million
Hydrogen bomb explosion	50,000

Where found	Degrees C
Surface of the Sun	7,000
Iron melts	1,500
Greenhouse Effect on Venus	400
Hottest place on Earth	58
Average on Earth's surface	20
Coldest place on Earth	-89
Temperature of universe	-270
Lowest temperature of liquids	-272.00001
Lowest temperaturae of metals	-272.00002
Absolute zero	-273.15

'We can never be sure what we are going to find at these supercold levels,' said another physicist, Robert Richardson, head of the low temperature physics group at Cornell University, Ithaca, New York. 'We seem to have stumbled upon an entirely new science.

'If the behaviour of a substance is to be studied at extremely low temperatures it must be liquid. Only two substances remain liquid near absolute zero: the isotopes helium-3 and helium-4. The first is the more interesting of the two, because it is the lighter and therefore moves around faster. It is thus ideal for studying the fundamental properties of matter.'

Pickett and his colleague Tony Guenault are studying the behaviour of 'superfluid' helium-3, a substance with a total absence of friction. It is expected to play an important role in providing stability and reliability to what may be world's largest solenoid magnets. Their collegues in the United States, meanwhile, are preparing to examine still more exotic phenomena.

One such mystery being studied by Richardson at Cornell is Werner Heisenberg's Uncertainty Principle of

1927, which states that some information is eternally unattainable. The speed and position of an electron cannot be determined simultaneously with absolute accuracy because the more we know of one, the less we can know of the other.

The behaviour of matter at supercold temperatures has much in common with its opposite in the realm of the extremely hot. Inside fast-spinning, superdense pulsar stars, where the heat exceeds 100 million degrees, matter is also in a superfluid state. Supercold helium will give astrophysicists an excellent idea of what happens inside these remnants of giant stars whose very atoms have been crushed out of existence.

The most bizarre of all phenomena which supercold matter is helping scientists to understand are 'cosmic strings'. These are believed to be strings of matter of huge mass but almost infinite thinness. An inch of such a string, according to Alexander Vilenkin, of Tufts University, Boston, would weigh 10 million billion tons. Such strings may still exist.

Millions of light-years long, their huge gravitaitonal attraction is believed to have formed the galaxies in the earliest epoch of the universe. Their superfluid behaviour is thought to be analogous to that of liquid helium near absolute zero. They may still exist.

But the most practical use for this refrigeration may be in high-speed computing by means of superconductivity. There is almost no 'noise' or resistance to an electric current at near absolute zero where atoms are so still, and a signal can travel unimpeded. The lower the temperature, the more thinking that can be done with less and less energy.

Brightest of the Bright

What is the difference in brightness between the brightest star and the faintest? This would make a good quiz question, but I will give the answer at once: the difference between the Sun, with an apparent magnitude of -26, and the faintest known stars that the Hubble Space Telescope can only see after an hour's time exposure, magnitude 30, encompasses a brightness ratio of more than 10^{22}, or 100 billion trillion.

The whole system of magnitudes, invented by Hipparchus in the second century BC, has become extremely complicated and is surely due for revision.

It seemed simple enough at first. The brightest stars, like the best athletes, were of the 'first magnitude' or the 'biggest', going down to the sixth. This worked well so long as nobody knew of any connection between distance and brightness, and so long as there were only six magnitudes. Ptolemy, four centuries later, slightly complicated matters by using the words 'greater' and 'smaller' to distinguish between stars within the same magnitude. But it was still Hipparchus's system.

Then Galileo's new telescope upset everything. 'With this new glass,' he proclaimed in 1610, 'you will detect below stars of the sixth magnitude such a crowd of others that escape natural sight that it is hardly believable.'

Today, with magnitudes down to at least 30 and all measured logarithmically (each magnitude is 2.512 times fainter than the last), the brightness of most classes of objects is well known. The full Moon is -12, a quarter Moon is -10, and Venus at its brightest is about -5. Sirius is -2, Vega is 0 (implying, confusingly, that Vega has no magnitude at all), and the naked eye limit is of course 6.

Beyond that, binoculars can distinguish stars down to 9, amateur telescopes down to 14, and a five-metre to 20. The Hubble can see magnitudes of 24 and fainter.

But how bright are distant stars in reality? *Absolute* magnitude provides that answer, by assuming that we see them at a theoretical distance of 32.6 light-years. By this scale the Sun is a mere 4.85 while Rigel is a dazzling -8. (I'm glad I do not live too close to Rigel.)

On top of this, we have *photographic* magnitude, showing how bright stars seemed on black and white film, and a new kind of magnitude based on the difference between a star's natural appearance and its photographic magnitude called the 'colour index'.

Add to that *bolometric* magnitude (a name based on an ancient device called a bolometre) which measures a star's total radiation, in all wavelengths except radio. Astronomers say this is the simplest classification that can be devised, but I have my doubts.

Meanwhile here is another quiz question. If it is true that a network of telescopes on the Moon will have 100,000 times the resolution of the Hubble, what will be the faintest magnitude it will be able to detect? The answer, assuming a long time-exposure made possible by 14-day lunar nights, is a staggering 42. In short, when astronomers reach the Moon, the brightness ratio between brightest and faintest will be nearly 2.512^{68}, which is 10^{27} or 1 followed by 27 zeros.

Smallest of the Small

The 1957 film *The Incredible Shrinking Man* shows the hero – or rather the victim – suffering from an unexplained radiation accident which causes him to become inexorably smaller. First he is the size of his cat, then of an insect, and finally he vanishes. At this point, unfortunately, the film stops and, unlike the London University physicist Michael Green and his colleagues, we have no chance to explore the realms of the almost infinitely small.

These scientists are not concerned even with the structure of atoms, but with 'superstrings', objects that compare in size with atoms as an atom compares with a planet. With a diameter in centimetres of 10^{-33}, a decimal point followed by 33 noughts and then a 1 – the Planck constant – superstrings form the bedrock of all matter.

Everything is made of them, including the supposedly empty space between the stars. They are the smallest objects that can exist. 'Without them, nothing else would exist,' Green said. 'There would be neither time nor space nor matter. There would be no stars or planets. There would be no universe.'

'The theory of superstrings is beautiful, wonderful, majestic – and strange,' says his colleague, Edward Witten of Princeton University. 'But it's not weird.'

At the level of superstrings, there is a world of unbelievable turbulence, of tossing and foaming and continuous change. In the words of John Wheeler of the University of Texas, Austin: 'Space is like an ocean which looks flat to the aviator who flies above it, but which is a tossing turmoil to the hapless butterfly which falls upon it. Regarded more and more closely, it shows more and more agitation until the structure is permeated everywhere with strings and holes. Einstein's general theory of relativity forces this foam-like character on all space.'

Why should these mysterious superstrings exist? There is no experimental evidence for them and, given their size, there may never be. Despite the scepticism of many physicists, Green and John Schwarz, of Princeton, devoted the Eighties to pursuing the superstring. 'I never worked with such intensity in my life,' says Green. 'I've never been so immersed in a subject.'

Green was eventually able to tell a meeting of the British Association for the Advancement of Science that he had at last reached the definite conclusion that superstrings are the only elegant way to reconcile the two principal theories that have underpinned twentieth-century physics: one that predicts the behaviour of planets, stars and galaxies, the other that describes the sub-atomic world.

The first of these, Einstein's general theory, states that the gravity of a planet (or any large mass) creates the time and space surrounding it. In other words, time and space have a physical structure as real as that of matter.

The other theory, of quantum mechanics, describes three of the fundamental forces of the universe which operate at extremely small distances: electromagnetism; the weak nuclear force that causes radioactivity; and the strong nuclear force that binds atoms.

But quantum mechanics says nothing about gravity, the fourth and weakest of the fundamental forces, which seems to work without needing any quantum esoterics to explain it. Yet gravitational waves, although felt across vast distances – by stars holding planets in their orbits – must travel.

By introducing the concept of the 'graviton', a particle that transmits gravity just as a photon transmits light, Green and Schwarz have been able to explain how superstrings work. At the tiny distances of the superstring world, gravity distorts and twists everything. It is responsible for the continuous turbulence that Wheeler describes.

Some mathematics even more abstruse than this suggests also that, in the very early universe, a few fractions of a second after the Big Bang, there were ten dimensions instead of the familiar four (length, breadth, height and time) we know today. The other six dimensions are still there. But in the words of physicist Gary Taubes, 'they remained curled up like rosebuds that never bloomed, locked in tight geometries of the immeasurably small.'

Yet this means that at the instant of the Big Bang all ten dimensions would have been, in some manner, equal. They would have been responsible for all four fundamental forces. Thus, superstring theory provides a grand unity of the forces, a 'theory of everything'.

But will the theory ever be of any practical use? 'We must be cautious in saying that it won't,' Green said. 'Remember how Rutherford, who split the atom, described the idea of usable atomic energy as "moonshine" . . .'

An Odyssey of the Sun

D id the earliest humans, when they looked up into African skies three million years ago, see the same Sun as we do? The difference would have been almost impossible to detect. But it was there none the less, for the size and brightness of the Sun has increased by a third since its formation some 5,000 million years ago. This process is going to continue until it eventually grows so huge that it will eat up the inner planets Mercury and Venus and come close to devouring the Earth.

Last week three astronomers announced the results of their 'Odyssey of the Sun'. They had fed the vital statistics of our parent star into a computer, programmed the machine to understand the laws of thermonuclear fusion, and foretold its vast and mysterious future.

'Predictions about the future of the Sun have been made before,' said one of them, Arnold Boothroyd, of the University of Toronto. 'But ours is superior because it was the first to be tailor-made for the Sun itself, rather than some hypothetical Sun-like star. We used all the correct numbers. We fed in its radius, mass, age, surface temperature and known composition. And then we told the machine to prophesy its future.'

Their findings foretell a series of stellar adventures, each stranger than the last, that can only be called an odyssey of the skies. The most unpleasant surprise is that the Earth will only be habitable for a quarter of the time than had been expected. It had been supposed that 5,000 million years – a time equal to the Sun's past age – would elapse before its growing heat became intolerable to terrestrial life. But the computer model reveals that we shall have to start evacuating Earth within a 'mere' 1,100 million years, as the Sun brightens by another 10 per cent and its ever increasing heat drives all the carbon dioxide out of our atmosphere. Without photosynthesis, plant life will perish and it will be time for humans to migrate from this barren rock.

Some 2,400 million years after this the Sun will have started to exhaust the supply of hydrogen fuel in its core, which will have been creating energy steadily for all these billions of years as it was being converted into helium. Now the helium itself starts to undergo nuclear burning, and the Sun grows even bigger, and now redder.

'The expanding Sun will stop just short of eating up the Earth and Moon – another surprise finding,' said Boothroyd. 'It will have become a "red giant" star with a diameter 200

times what it is at present and a brightness some 5,000 times greater. But here the expansion must end. Because it is a star of comparatively small mass, its helium will not become hot enough to ignite and burn to become another element. Instead, because of this lack of further fuel to burn, the Sun will throw out mass that will form into vast rings of luminous gas and dust thousands of millions of kilometres around it.'

Unable to expand any further, the Sun must now contract. Within a period of about 100 million years, its nuclear fuel exhausted, it will shrink to the size of the Earth, a mere 13,000 kilometes in diameter, but with three-quarters of the Sun's original mass squashed into it. This will make it a 'white dwarf' star, an object so dense that a piece of its material the size of a matchbox will weigh about ten tons. Icko Iben, of the University of Illinois at Urbana-Champagne, said: 'This will be an extraordinary object, faint, half planet and half star, still smouldering from the remains of the nuclear power in its core. About a fifth of the stars in our Milky Way galaxy are such white dwarfs.

'Its gravitational compression will be so strong that mountain ranges on its surface will be no more than a few inches high. Any astronaut who ventures to tread on it will be instantly squashed flat. Yet it will still have an atmosphere about half a mile thick.'

Another 1,000 million years pass, and all nuclear activity has ceased. The Sun has lost all luminosity and has become a 'black dwarf'. It will retain its density but be invisible. While not to be confused with a black hole, it will have something of its character, for it will be an object of deadly peril to astronauts who, unaware of its existence, might become trapped in its orbit.

An incredible journey, indeed, and a terrible inevitable fate for the sole source of warmth and life on Earth – and, of course, for Earth itself.

Going Bats in the Basement

Science, like many other activities, is a random mixture of the sublime and the ridiculous. Seldom has this combination been more apparent than in an extraordinary correspondence in an American journal about the creation of new universes.

This speculation has been brought right down to earth with a statement in the journal *Science* by Alan Guth, a physicist at the Massachusetts Institute of Technology, who says: 'We now have the tools to seriously discuss the prospect of creating a universe in your own basement.'

To most people space is just empty nothingness. But to physicists, this statement ceases to be true at the sub-sub-sub-microscopic level. If we could examine empty space of a hundred-millionth of a trillionth of a trillionth of a millimetre, (on the scale of Planck's Constant), we would find a cauldron of activity. It would be full of interconnecting 'worm-holes', through which objects would vanish into the past or future. To Guth and many of his colleagues, these 'worm-holes' are the gateways to other universes, regions that might not be microscopic at all. A person who compressed himself to a tiny size, like Alice going through a very small looking-glass, would find himself in an expanding region with dimensions which were of light-years in extent. (See Through a Wormhole to the Stars?, p. 234.) Hence the professor's bold and quite serious conclusion that new universes may be constantly coming into existence, even in the empty space of one's basement.

So much for sublimity: now for the ridicule. Howard Topoff, a psychologist from Hunter College, New York City University, has written this reply to Guth in *Science*. 'I was particularly interested to learn that mathematical tools are now available to create a universe in the basement. I was able to locate an empty room in the basement of Hunter College, and I persuaded several colleagues to join me in creating a new universe during Dean's hours on Wednesday afternoon.

'But we encountered numerous theoretical problems: Hunter College is short of space. Since the newly created universe is expected to expand exponentially, the problem of finding intergalactic space must first be discussed with administration.

'Who will be Dean of the universe, and will it be run on hard or soft money? What if new life emerges within this universe? Hunter College is unionized, and so it would be very difficult not to grant tenure to any new life-form, regardless of its chemical basis.

'What if the universe was composed of (violently explosive) anti-matter? It would be just my dumb luck to have a universe expand out of the basement up to the sixth floor, and annihilate the psychology department. Isn't it enough to have to worry about perishing for lack of publishing?

'Our conclusion is that it is currently much too dangerous to attempt the creation of a new universe in the basement. If at all possible, we recommend the roof instead.'

Running Water on Mars

Water in liquid form exists on the surface of Mars. This discovery – a crucial advance in planetary science – removes one of the great obstacles to establishing settlements on the Red Planet. It also increases the probability that primitive life exists there although it does not prove it. If, in fact, this were proved it would be an epochal event – the first discovery of life beyond Earth.

But first, the evidence for Martian water. It has been discovered, not by a space probe, but by an examination of meteorites which once lay on the surface of Mars and have fallen to Earth. This is caused by a large asteroid striking Mars. Stones lying on the planet's surface are thrown into space by the 'splash' of the impact. They fly around the solar system for a few million years and then, sometimes, land here.

Thomas Donahue of Michigan University at Ann Arbor explained, in *Nature* magazine, how studies of a large number of these meteorites showed that the air in the thin Martian atmosphere is interacting with water at its surface. For these meteorites contain hydrous, or water-bearing, minerals. The ratio in them between two types of hydrogen, light and heavy, proves that water is coming to the surface and evaporating.

'The rest of the water will not be far below,' says Donahue. 'If it was spread on the surface uniformly, it would cover Mars to a depth of 25 metres. All that colonists on Mars will need to do is sink wells to get it out. This will make the establishment of settlements much easier and cheaper than it has seemed until now.'

However, Mars is an extremely cold and dry world. Where did all this water come from?

It is already known from the shape of basins on its surface, especially in its northern hemisphere, that some three billion years ago it was much warmer than it is today, and that it had widespread oceans and rivers. Then there occurred some vast cosmic accident which ruined Mars as a habitable world. Perhaps a massive asteroid strike pushed the planet out to an orbit much further from the Sun – where it now remains – and, as Mars grew colder, much of this water evaporated.

But, not all. The rest would have drained away underground. Until now, it was thought to lie in the form of deeply frozen ice which future colonists would have to melt, perhaps by atomic explosions. The new discovery, that the water is easily available without such industrial violence, is a most encouraging surprise.

There remains the possibility of life. Donahue speculates: 'With water trickling to the surface, there is always the possibility that microbial creatures could exist at the bottom of some crater.'

Although the experiments on Mars of the Viking lander in 1976 found no trace of life – only of chemical reactions – there are clues in other Martian meteorites that have landed on Earth, in the form of amino acids, the chemical building blocks which comprise the most basic proteins that form living tissue. Whilst this does not 'prove' that there is life on Mars – as amino acids are only the ingredients of life, not life itself – conversely, neither does it disprove the life-on-Mars theory. All we can say is that life may be present on Mars now, or it may have been there three billion years ago – but we don't know if either or both of these beliefs are correct.

The trouble is that nobody knows how long the amino acid meteorite had been flying through space before it fell to Earth. Was it ejected from the Red Planet when our ape-like ancestors were making their first tools, or did it first fly at a far earlier epoch when life was only beginning to appear here?

Was it, in short, the product of today's frigid Mars, or of a lush, comparatively warmer planet? These speculations aside, within a half-century from now there is likely to be advanced life on Mars – our own. Whether we find microbes or not, easily accessible water will enable future settlers to turn it into a permanent second world for mankind.

The Great Comets

I n the summer of 1995 there appeared over the Andes an
unusually bright comet never hitherto recorded. Although
easily visible to the naked eye, this seventeenth such discovery – found by the Australian William Bradfield, the
world's most successful comet-hunter – was not even
reported in the northern hemisphere press because it could
only be seen below the equator.

New comets are not especially remarkable. They appear
on average three times a year. Yet the science of comets is
fascinating, since the comets surrounding the Sun almost
outnumber the stars in the Milky Way.

About a light-year away lies a vast belt of at least
200,000 million comets known as the Oort Cloud, debris
left over from the formation of the solar system five billion
years ago. The nucleus of each is no longer than a few
kilometres, but their combined mass would create a planet
100 times heavier than the Earth.

Periodically they fly inwards towards the Sun at the
prompting of unknown gravitational disturbances. To such
events we owe Comet Shoemaker Levy 9 which crashed into
Jupiter, and the approaching Hale-Bopp, which promises to
be a tremendous sight. It could rival the great comet of
1811, mentioned in Tolstoy's *War and Peace*, and famous
because in Russian folklore it presaged the invasion of
Napoleon. The chances of this particular comet hitting
Earth were always very low. In fact it missed us by more
than a million kilometres.

The comet of 1811 was also the only comet to be associated with port wine. In that year, for some unrelated reason, the vintage in Portugal was unusually good and wine merchants displayed it as 'Comet Port'.

The only brighter comet was that of 1843, perhaps less famous because it had no link with military or political legend. It was also the biggest, with a tail-length estimated

at 300 million kilometres, greater than the distance between the Sun and the orbit of Mars.

Patrick Moore, in the 1995 fifth edition of his *Guinness Book of Astronomy,* lists some of history's famous comets. The closest known approach to Earth – always a subject of alarm since it may have been a comet's impact that killed the dinosaurs 65 million years ago – was that of Lexell's Comet of 1770 which passed within two million kilometres of us, only five times the distance to the Moon. But its orbit was changed nine years later by a close approach to Jupiter, and it may never be seen again.

The most frequently seen comet is Encke, which returns to Earth's vicinity every 3.3 years. In 1979 it suffered a 'change of sex' – it was found to have lost its snow and gaseous tail and turned into a stony asteroid. Many asteroids are likely to be comets which have 'burned out'. And the comet least often seen is Finsler's of 1937. Its period – the time between its appearances – has been calculated at 13.6 million years, so that it last appeared long before there were people to observe it.

The 'tail' of a comet is a misleading term. When the comet travels away from the Sun, it is preceded by its tail which consists of gas and dust blown off it by sunlight. Some rare comets have more than one tail.

There is a remarkable history of cometary superstitions. Before it was known that they appeared so often, it was easy to associate them with the adventures of great leaders. One came at the time of Julius Caesar's assassination. In Shakespeare's play of that title, the dictator's wife remarks on it with the alarmed observation:

When beggars die, there are no comets seen;
The heavens themselves blaze forth the death of princes.

Another was seen by the emperor Vespasian in AD 79. He

dismissed it, calling it 'hairy' (as all tailed comets seem to be), remarking that it 'menaced rather the King of the Parthians, for he is hairy while I am bald'. But Vespasian died in the same year. Another Roman emperor, Macrinus, died in 218, the year of a visit by Halley's Comet whose later appearance in 1066 was used with great political effect by William the Conqueror.

Some advanced thinkers have proposed that comets could one day be used as spaceships. They have many advantages for such a purpose: speed, free propulsion, and storage space for people and cargo. The only disadvantage is that they would be difficult to steer.

The Most Accurate Clock

The most accurate clock in the universe is so precise that it will lose or gain only one second in three million years.

It is no work of man, but one of a class of extraordinary celestial objects called 'millisecond pulsars'. These are collapsed stars that spin faster than aircraft propellers and are so densely packed with matter that a tennis ball made of the same stuff would weigh more than 20,000 million tons.

The density and speed of rotation are directly connected. As a general rule, the more densely packed an object is in space the more rapidly it will rotate. This 'super-clock' rotates six thousand times a second with almost absolute reliability, emitting radio beeps as it does so, making it more than ten times more accurate than the atomic clocks that regulate Earth time.

The fastest of the millisecond pulsars is fascinating astronomers: it is known somewhat prosaically as PSR 1937 + 21, a name that describes its position in the sky 10,000 light-years away in space. Says one of Britain's leading cosmologists, Martin Rees, of the Institute of Astronomy at Cambridge: 'If the Earth were to rotate much faster than it does, then centrifugal force would soon cause it to break up and fly apart in all directions. The fact that these pulsars do *not* fly apart, despite their speeds of rotation, proves that they must be tremendously dense with almost unimaginably strong gravitational fields holding them together.'

Such pulsars were once stars like the Sun but very much

larger. Being so huge they used up their nuclear fuel at a profligate rate and exploded as cataclysmically violent 'supernovae', blasting their outer layers out into space at speeds of more than 50,000 kilometres per second – nearly a fifth of the speed of light. Their inner cores then collapsed under their own weight, reducing a star that might once have been three million kilometres wide to a super-dense object perhaps 15 kilometres in diameter – the estimated size of PSR 1937 + 21.

All sorts of practical uses are being proposed for this cosmic clock. 'We could use it to make much more accurate measurements of the solar system,' says Andrew Lyne, of Manchester University. 'All the clocks on Earth, even the atomic clocks are biased by various gravitational fields. The tidal pull of the Sun, for example, slows down and speeds up clocks on Earth by very small amounts. But PSR 1937 + 21 is subjected to no gravitational influences other than its own. It is alone in space, not in orbit around another star. Its measurement of time is therefore absolutely without bias.

'As the Earth moves around the Sun it is sometimes approaching this remote pulsar and at other times receding from it. Because of the way radio waves behave the pulsar's beeps will differ accordingly. From this, we should be able to calculate the Earth's position – and the orbits of all the other planets with an accuracy never before achieved.'

Daniel Stinebring of Princeton University outlines even more practical future uses for the pulsar.

'We could use it for the navigational guidance of inter-planetary spacecraft, where even the tiniest error can put a craft hundreds of kilometres off course,' he says. 'And I believe it may eventually replace the atomic clocks we now use.'

It is fortunate that this pulsar is so far away. Pulsars are 'cannibal' stars, with magnetic fields more than a million times stronger than the Earth's, whose gravity devours any other star with which it is in orbit. A pulsar that came too close to the Sun would doom humanity.

Another recently discovered millisecond pulsar, PSR 1957 + 20, is ripping apart the star it is orbiting. The unfortunate star's outer layers are being 'eaten away', says Professor Stinebring. This star, which might once have been as massive as the Sun, will vanish in a few million years. The pulsar, having entirely devoured it, will continue to spin as before, keeping absolutely accurate time.

There's Nobody Here

I s there life on Earth? Or anywhere else for that matter? Even if the Galaxy were filled with *Star Trek*-like alien ships, they might be unable to recognize us.

An experiment using photographs of the Earth taken by Nasa's Galileo spacecraft from a mere 1,000 kilometres found not a single indication of the existence of intelligent life – a result that seems amazing in the light of our ever growing technology.

'If that spacecraft had been sent by a group of alien scientists from another planet, nothing in these pictures would prove to them that this world was the abode of intelligent creatures,' said one of them, W. Reid Thompson, of Cornell University, New York, co-author of a paper in *Nature*.

'All they show is white clouds, the blue of the oceans, and the brown outlines of South America and Australia. Neither cities nor agricultural fields can be identified as artificial objects, since their rectangular shapes are undetectable. The spacecraft might see the glint of sunlight from satellites and large aircraft, and it might observe aircraft contrails. But the "conservatives" among the alien scientists – in any scientific debate there are always "conservatives" and "radicals" – could all too plausibly insist that these phenomena were merely cosmic rays striking their own detectors.'

But what if the spacecraft photographed the planet at night (which Galileo did not)? 'I think they could explain the lights of cities as natural fires or lowly phosphorescent organisms with whom it would not be worth communicating.

'Since our languages would be unintelligible to them, and perhaps not even recognizable as languages, they might even mistake our radio and television signals for natural radio activity. Similarly, the oxygen in our atmosphere might be considered, not as supportive of life but as poisonous to it.'

The moral is that we should not be too hasty to conclude that other planets and moons in the solar system, of which more than 60 have been surveyed by our spacecraft, were necessarily lifeless. 'When looking at other planets close-up, one should always examine that extra bit of data, even if the

227

exercise might at first sight seem pointless. For example, Saturn's giant moon Titan, which has a rich methane atmosphere, may well contain the building blocks of life,' said Reid Thompson.

The *Nature* team were 'radicals' who believe that the Galaxy contains perhaps millions of advanced civilizations. But a scientist of the rival 'conservative' school, Richard Teske, of the University of Michigan at Ann Arbor, argued in the *Quarterly Journal of the Royal Astronomical Society* that these must be extremely rare in the Galaxy.

Teske said: 'The Earth is the only planet in our solar system that is highly active geologically. Having valuable metals close to the surface and easily minable gives us our high technology. If our precious metals were buried deeper, as is the case with the planet Mercury, then we would not have advanced much beyond the eighteenth century.'

This would explain the surprising negative findings of Paul Horowitz of Harvard, who failed to detect any intelligent radio signals from any planet within 25 light-years of the Earth. Ominously for the radicals, this region of 65,000 cubic light-years around the Earth contains no fewer than 12 stars that are similar to the Sun. If Sun-like stars cannot produce advanced civilizations in their orbits, what other stars will?

So what makes the Earth unique? Scientists at the Bureau des Longitudes in Paris have produced a surprising answer. They found that the Moon's gravitational field keeps the Earth's climate stable by moderating its axial tilt. It must be highly unusual in the Galaxy for an Earth-sized planet to have so large a moon, and be at the right distance from its parent star.

A Corridor Both Curved and Straight

Alice, transported from Wonderland to a black hole in space, would be at home to find that a corridor can be straight and curved at the same time.

'Imagine a manned space station in the form of a ring that encircles a black hole,' says Marek Abramowicz of Göteborg University, Sweden, in the *Scientific American*. 'The corridor can curve inwards, outwards or be absolutely straight. It depends on the distance of the ring from the hole.'

From the outside, it will look like a ring, but to Alice the Astronaut the corridor will adopt different shapes. If it is at a critical distance from the hole – one and a half times the radius of the black hole itself – Alice would see its corridor as absolutely straight ahead of her and (if she dared look) behind her.

'Imagine that she attaches a lamp to the roof of the corridor and then walks away from it,' writes Abramowicz. 'As she looks behind her, she sees the lamp become progressively dimmer, but never obscured from view by any bend in the corridor. Finally, she peers forward and sees the lamp become progressively brighter. In fact, the image from the lamp circulates round the tube many times, so she sees multiple images of it.

'Although she might have difficulty explaining why the lamp appears both behind and in front of her, she must conclude that the curved tube is straight because its walls never obscure the lamp.'

The explanation is that space itself around the black hole is warped – and so is the path taken by light. A light-ray, trying in vain to escape from the hole, would orbit the hole in a perfect circle at this critical distance. And because humans are equipped to perceive light as travelling in straight lines, the ray's curved path would appear to Alice as perfectly straight.

In a larger ring, the warping would be negligible, and the corridor would curve inwards. But if it was closer, then the hole's stronger gravity would pull it inwards so that centrifugal force would make it curve outwards. '"Inward" and "outward" are not absolute concepts,' Abramowicz adds. 'They become relative when space is warped.'

The Multi-coloured Cosmos

The universe, when properly seen, is a riot of colour. Yet it does not always appear so. Amateurs are often disappointed that when they look into the night sky with binoculars, they see only a uniform black and white.

Happily, this is only an illusion caused by the fact that they are using their eyes instead of a camera lens. As a series of articles in *Astronomy Now* reminded us, every celestial object, whether star, planet or moon, has its own particular colour. The result is a blaze of multi-coloured light that makes the view of the most garish city from an aircraft window look dull.

The colour of a star depends on its surface temperature. We can visualize this by heating a poker in a fire. At first it glows orange. A little hotter and it becomes red. And if the fire was hot enough, the poker would turn white. At the highest possible temperatures, impossible in an ordinary fire, it would be blue-hot.

Temperature is in turn is related to the star's age. A star will start its life at superheat and will gradually cool through time. The hottest stars tend to be the youngest and the coolest are usually the oldest. The hottest stars, like Rigel, with surface temperatures of up to 160,000F, are bright blue. Then come the brilliant white stars like Sirius (with a tinge of blue) at about 20,000F.

Cooler still are Sun-like stars with temperatures of 12,000F. Then we are down to red giants, such as Aldebaran, 30 times bigger than the Sun, and a mirror of

what the Sun will become in about five billion years, when the exhaustion of its nuclear fuel makes it swell up. Aldebaran is no more than 6,000F. One star of this class has been described by an astronomer as 'gleaming like a crimson jewel'.

But after the red giant stage, the star can get hotter again. Gravity takes over and it collapses, until most of its original mass is compressed into a body the size of the Earth. This is a white dwarf, a thimble-full of whose material would weigh about ten tons. It is literally white-hot, since the pressure of its density has driven up its temperature to some 10,000F.

The colours of the planets are just as striking, although for chemical rather than nuclear reasons. The skies of Mars, for example, are orange-red because of the ochre-red iron dust from the surface driven into the atmosphere by dust storms.

The Moon has two distinct shades, dark and light, created by its differing rock compositions. The dark regions, or 'seas', are basalt, the result of ancient lava floes, and made of iron, magnesium and titanium. The lighter parts – which future tourists will find easier to walk on – are rich in calcium and aluminium.

The four gas giants, Jupiter, Saturn, Uranus and Neptune, are all similar in general composition, yet they have different colours. Jupiter has brown strips across a greenish background and the enigmatic Great Red Spot. Yet Saturn is much whiter. This may be because it has less mass than Jupiter, with weaker surface gravity. Its clouds are therefore proportionately deeper than Jupiter's, making them reflect sunlight more evenly. Both Uranus and Neptune are of a startling blue. Their atmospheres are so cold, since they are so far from the Sun, that they consist largely of clouds of freezing methane which absorb the red part of the Sun's light.

Yet the real beauty of the heavens comes from celestial objects that do not yet exist! These are the great clouds of dust and gas – mostly hydrogen – the source material of stars which are yet to be and the relics of stars that once were. One such is the Vela supernova remnant. It exploded about 11,000 years ago and may have inspired our Ice Age ancestors to wonder at the heavens.

Through a Wormhole to the Stars?

Through hyperspace, that unimaginable region that was neither space nor time, matter nor energy, something nor nothing, one could traverse the length of the galaxy in the interval between two neighbouring instants of time.

Isaac Asimov, *The Foundation Trilogy*

F ew science fiction novels dealing with interstellar adventure would make much sense without the 'Jumps' though 'hyperspace' that enable spaceships to treat the cosmos as though it were little more than the London Underground. Until recently, however, physicists have tended to dismiss such journeys as fantasy.

But how convenient they would be! Defying the rule that forbids faster-than-light journeys, our descendants could travel to the nearest star system to the sun Alpha Centauri, within weeks, and colonize all the habitable planets in our Milky Way galaxy in a few tens of millennia.

Hyperspace travel may not be fantasy after all. An article in the *New Scientist* reports that great theoretical progress has been made in the subject since 1989 when two physicists, Michael Morris and Kip Thorne, published a paper that was inspired by an effort to help Carl Sagan make his novel *Contact* sound plausible.

The keys to the matter are 'wormholes' in the structure of space-time, which supposedly link up regions of space in a tunnel-system of unimaginable complexity. According to the equations of Einstein's 1916 general theory of relativity, space–time has a solid structure. Massive objects such as stars and planets create the space and time that surround them.

The entrances to these tunnels exist everywhere, but – and here is the catch – their diameter is so small that they would make atoms seem as large as planets. They are as tiny as it is physically possible for anything to be, no wider than a billionth of a trillionth of a trillionth of a centimetre.

There are therefore three ways to imagine hyperspace travel. One is to shrink the spaceship and crew down to this size (and enlarge them again when they re-emerge into ordinary space), which seems a hopeless proposition. The second is to enlarge a wormhole to reasonable size by some exotic mechanism, such as repulsive – as opposed to attractive – gravity, which seems very difficult. And the third, proposed by Richard Gott, of Princeton University, and John Cramer, of Washington State University at Pullman, is to search for reasonable-sized wormholes *which may already exist*.

This idea comes from the history of the universe itself. When it was created by the Big Bang some 15 billion years ago, its size was infinitessimal. How, then, did it become so vast? The answer accepted by many physicists is 'inflation' which, within a few fractions of a second, used repulsive gravity to expand the cosmos to its present size. This tremendous enlargement, which made *everything* bigger, might also have enlarged primordial wormholes, from the sub-sub-microscopic size that we today imagine them, to diameters of thousands, if not millions of miles.

The next step is to find such a wormhole. This requires little extra effort to what many astronomers routinely do – to monitor thousands of millions of stars for many years to see if their light fluctuates in a particularly unusual manner.

Starlight fluctuates in many ways, from many different causes, but Morris believes that a wormhole that passed between a star and ourselves would make the star shine in a highly peculiar way. He calculates that if held apart by repulsive gravity (as a large-sized wormhole would have to be) it would force the light of the star behind it to emit 'twin spikes' of light with a dimness in the middle. Existing stellar images could easily enable us to seek such exotically shining stars.

However, wormhole tunnels, whether large or small, are likely to be extremely complex. Theory predicts that travelling through them will be no easy matter, for they will divide and sub-divide in a manner vastly more intricate than the most cunningly dug Roman catacomb. There will be junction upon junction, loop upon loop, until the chances of *not* getting lost becomes infinitessimal.

Nobody, in short, has the slightest idea how one could navigate through such a labyrinth. As far as we can understand wormholes today, there would be no means of knowing not only *where* we would emerge, but even *when*.

Some theories (but not all) predict that the travellers would go backwards in time. They would then have to re-emerge into ordinary space in another universe since it would be impossible to return to the past of this one. Why? Because they would then be able to murder their own parents before they met, creating a forbidden paradox. (See The Tunnel of Time, p. 240.)

Starship designers will therefore have to decide whether to stick to ordinary space and comparatively slow speeds, or to attempt to exploit a science that may prove prohibitively complex.

The Biggest Blasts

For half a century, physicists have been trying to build more destructive nuclear bombs. Their efforts are puny compared with those of nature, which creates explosions that could shatter the Solar System. These are supernovae, the colossal blasts in which certain kinds of stars end their lives, blazing forth for several months with the light of many billions of suns.

Until a few months ago, astrophysicists had only the most general ideas of why supernovae explode. But now detailed studies with a super-computer, reported recently to the American Astronomical Society, show precisely how these tremendous detonations occur.

The moment of destruction comes when a star at least eight times more massive than the Sun has exhausted its nuclear fuel. It started off, billions of years before, being largely composed of hydrogen, the lightest of gases. Through the eons, in a series of thermonuclear reactions, the hydrogen is converted into one element after another, each heavier than the last, including diamonds, otherwise known as carbon. Finally only iron remains which, being entirely stable, cannot be converted into anything else.

These reactions can be roughly described by my verse:

Hydrogen to helium will give you a suntan,
Helium to carbon will make you very rich.
Carbon to silicon does nothing in particular,
But silicon to iron will blow you to bits.

'The explosion is triggered within a fraction of a second in a mechanism that has three distinct stages,' said Marc Herant, of the Los Alamos National Laboratory in New Mexico.

The first of these comes when the core of the giant star is entirely composed of iron. No longer able to hold itself apart by nuclear 'burning', it collapses on itself. The outer layer of the core crashes down upon the inner. No less than 3,000 trillion trillion tons of iron slam together at speeds of 322 million kilometres per hour. Within a tenth of a second, the core has shrunk from a diameter of thousands of kilometres to one of about 20.

At this stage, the core is still surrounded by an 'envelope' of gases left over from previous reactions. Part of the envelope now begins to 'rain' down on the core. Within this gaseous rain are almost massless particles, neutrinos and anti-neutrinos. These particles are so tiny that they do not normally collide with atoms at all. In theory, they could travel through a solid wall of lead ten light-years thick without hitting anything. But not so with this super-compressed iron core. It is so dense that a piece of it the size of a sugar cube weighs ten billion tons.

The anti-neutrinos now collide with iron atoms. Everywhere in the core, are explosions of matter and anti-matter in which Einstein's equation $E=mc^2$ works with 100 per cent efficiency. The temperature of the core rises to several hundred billion degrees. But the remainder of the gaseous envelope still surrounds it. The core, bursting with energy, is like a pressure cooker with no safety valve which finally bursts the envelope, and the star explodes with cataclysmic violence.

Yet supernovae are not entirely destructive. Religiously minded people might think them part of God's plan. For without them there would be no chance of life anywhere.

Only the relatively useless elements of hydrogen and helium are made without them. Supernovae spew out into space all the heavier elements that make up our bodies and needs.

They give us oxygen to breathe, carbon for our plant life, calcium for our bones, nitrogen for our agriculture, iron for our machines, silicon for our computer chips, neon for our advertizing and nickel for our coins. The next star likely to explode as a supernova is the red giant Betelgeuse, which is at the safe distance of 300 light-years away. 'For a few months Betelgeuse will be brighter than the full Moon,' said Herant. 'It will also be more dangerous to look at than the Moon because so much brilliant light will be concentrated in a single point source.'

Betelgeuse will not explode in the immediate future. Supernovae explode at a rate of approximately one per galaxy per century. But since there are at least 100 billion galaxies, they must be exploding, far beyond the vision of even our most powerful telescopes, at a rate of about one per second. We may live in a much more violent – and life-producing – universe than we imagine.

The Tunnel of Time

J ust to conceive of travelling into the past, like the hero of H.G. Wells's novel, *The Time Machine*, you have to take leave of your senses.

Well, your common sense at least. Because to do so you must enter a world of many different realities where, at the end of the day, you bump up against that familiar but terrifying entity called a black hole.

'Common sense may rule out time travel, but the laws of physics do not,' say David Deutsch and Michael Lockwood, two Oxford physicists in *Scientific American*. 'If it is impossible, then the reason has yet to be discovered. It is incumbent on anyone who still wants to reject the idea to come up with some new scientific argument.'

There is no great obstacle to travelling into the future. One could put oneself into a super-sophisticated deep-freeze with instructions to be awakened in 100 or 1,000 years, or travel in a spaceship almost at the speed of light, in which time would slow down and where, at the end of the journey, one would be at a period in the future dictated by the speed at which one had travelled. But in no circumstances, so it has been believed until now, could one reverse direction like Wells's Time Traveller. For that would be travel into the past.

The rule has been that one can *observe* the past but that *interference* with it is forbidden, a rule easily obeyed by watching an old newsreel. Interference with the past, it was said, would create an impossible paradox. A man could go back and murder his parents before they met, in which case he would not only cease to exist but cease ever to have existed. But if he never existed, who committed the murders?

This is a reason why it is impossible to travel faster than light. The closer a spaceship gets to that speed, the slower time inside it runs. At the speed of light itself, time would stop altogether. Faster than that it would run backwards – a scenario which recalls the verses:

There was a young lady called Bright,
Who travelled much faster than light.
She started one day
In the relative way
And returned on the previous night.

The lady was Bright but not bright,
And she joined in next day in the flight;
So then two made the date,
And then four and then eight,
And her spouse got the hell of a fright.

All these Mrs Brights exist because each, on returning home, meets an untravelled version of herself. But what happens if the first traveller tells her stay-at-home clone that the journey was disagreeable and she should cancel her ticket? The traveller would both exist and not exist at the same time. Or perhaps the universe, its laws having been violated, would quietly disappear.

This view correctly represents what Deutsch and Lockwood call the 'classical view', which prevailed until 1957, when the late Hugh Everett proposed his famous 'Many Worlds theorem' of quantum mechanics, suggesting that at every instant since the birth of the universe, reality has been branching into different realities.

There is one reality in which your parents married, and countless others in which they never met. You can travel back to meet them but because, by the very act of meeting them, you can prevent their marriage, they cannot be the parents that gave birth to you. If they were you would not exist. They will be two other people, in another reality, subtly different from this one. Paradox is thus avoided.

But how is it possible to travel backwards in time into a different reality? It is not just a matter of pressing a few levers on a complicated console like Wells's hero.

According to Amos Ori, a physicist at the California Institute of Technology, it can be done only by going through a black hole. He has shown that a spaceship trapped inside a fast-rotating black hole would not be crushed by overwhelming gravitational forces. The 'singularity' at the centre of the hole would be opened out by centrifugal force until it resembled a 'ring', the gateway to a tunnel through which the spaceship could pass.

'In a black hole, the warping of the fabric of space and time is so intense that the fabric tears itself apart,' says Deutsch. 'It rejoins itself, but in a different way, so a spaceship that emerges through that tunnel will travel backwards in time. It will be in another reality.'

It used to be supposed that no spaceship could make this journey, because the incoming light being trapped from outside the hole would be infinitely strong and would 'fry' the spaceship. But Ori has shown that this would not happen. The strength of the pursuing light would be too feeble to harm the spaceship. 'We are still not sure that our models of the interiors of fast-rotating black holes are correct, and whether they do create navigable 'rings'. But if they do, then the exits through the tunnel will be exits backward in time and into another reality.'

So what is the use of time travel? Well, it could make

international diplomacy much easier. 'Suppose,' says Deutsch, 'that two rival civilizations were struggling for possession of a galaxy. Instead of going to war, they could agree to go into separate realities and each would then have the galaxy to themselves.'

Moons Beyond Ours

Imagine walking on the most slippery ice possible, without dirt or rubble to give your feet a grip. Day and night, the inky black sky is filled with countless stars, while in one direction, just beyond the horizon, rises a curved yellow curtain so huge that it seems to fill the sky.

The curtain is the edge of the ringed planet Saturn, and we are standing on its moon Enceladus, whose crust seems to be made entirely of very pure ice.

Enceladus is one of the innumerable moons, planets, comets and asteroids of our Solar System that fill a spectacular paperback picture book, *The Grand Tour: A Traveller's Guide to the Solar System*, by Ron Miller and William K. Hartmann.

'What grandeur, desolation, power, silence, resources or loneliness do these places offer?' ask the authors, presenting us with the vast retinues of worlds and worldlets that orbit Saturn, the 'lord of the rings', and its giant companion planets.

The crew of an alien spacecraft visiting the Solar System would first encounter Pluto, normally the Sun's most distant world, from where the Sun is just a bright star, a pinpoint of light amid the Milky Way's star-clouds. It would be hard even to realize that the Sun is its parent star.

Pluto, whose years last 248 of ours, is an infinitely lonely place, so cold that its atmosphere is frozen as hard as steel. From its surface, the only large visible body is its moon Charon, so close that it appears in the sky 17 times the apparent size of Earth's moon.

Travelling sunwards from Pluto, the aliens would next visit Neptune and its large moon, Triton. Its icy surface lit with a faint blue light by the far-off Sun, Triton has the mysterious phenomenon – which no other moon or world is known to possess – of thick plumes of smoke shooting out from its interior. Perhaps only visiting astronauts will discover one day what causes them.

Sunwards again towards Miranda, one of the smallest but by far the most interesting moons of Uranus. The larger moons of Uranus are cratered and quite dull, but Miranda, with her parent planet swelling above like a blue-green balloon, has a unique phenomenon of her own, a not quite vertical cliff known as the Great Wall that rises sheer to a

height of many kilometres. Great boulders falling down it, say the book's authors, 'would take many minutes to reach the bottom, where they would roll on to the valley at the speed of fast trains'.

Saturn has a moon even stranger than Enceladus. This is Iapetus, the entrance to hyperspace in Arthur C. Clarke's novel *2001*. To telescopes on Earth, it is visible when on one side of Saturn, but vanishes when it passes to the other. This is because it has two 'faces'. One is permanently icy while the other, which always faces Saturn, is inexplicably black.

But the most bizarre, and also most violent, world in the Solar System is undoubtedly Jupiter's moon Io. It experiences two and a half hours of solar eclipse each day as the Sun goes behind Jupiter. With dozens of simultaneously erupting volcanoes, it is literally turning itself inside out, its surface being buried ever deeper beneath debris as new material is spewed out from its interior. These eruptions are caused by the proximity of massive Jupiter – only 100,000 kilometres away – whose gravitational field is perpetually convulsing its interior, creating volcanoes at random.

What will be the fate of these far-off worlds? Isaac Asimov once suggested that ice-covered Enceladus might eventually be propelled to Mars so that its water could irrigate that dry planet.

But smashing up one of the most beautiful of worlds in an infinitely wonderful Solar System may seem to our descendants too great an environmental crime.

Part Five

STRANGE
BELIEFS

Newton, 'Rapist' of the Universe

Why are there so few women scientists? The reason, says an expert on feminism, is not so much male prejudice as the influence of militant feminists who proclaim that science is a 'tool of domination'.

'These people, to whom ideology is all that matters, are driving women out of science by imposing their beliefs on them,' Noretta Koertge, a historian and philosopher of science at Indiana University in Bloomington, told a meeting of the American Association for the Advancement of Science in Atlanta.

'They claim that research is valueless unless it conforms to current ideology. If a woman scientist reveals her profession at a feminist gathering, she is likely to be told, "You're wicked. You're consorting with the enemy. You're raping the environment".'

At the centre of this ideology was a paranoid obsession with rape. The feminists, say Koertge and others, believe that pursuing knowledge is a violation of nature and hence that 'to seek to know is to want to f**k.'

One of them had asserted that Isaac Newton's *Principia*, which deals with the laws of gravitation, is a 'rape manual'. By this she had meant that this great work of mathematical exploration 'penetrated the innards' of physics.

Many female students had taken this literally. They were now convinced that the laws of gravity were about sex, and therefore shunned them. Other feminists had a special dislike of biology. They had convinced themselves that the

pain of childbirth was a 'social construction', meaning that it could be prevented by political reform.

'They claim that the biological classification of human beings into two sexes is inspired by the political desire to demarcate clearly those who are to dominate and those who are to be dominated. If this demarcation was changed – so they say – then it would no longer be painful to give birth.'

Koertge had heard a female would-be astronomer – who decided after all not be an astronomer – say she had changed her mind because she was put off by the expression 'Big

Bang', which describes the violent origin of the universe. Such 'male sexist terminology', said the sensitive creature, 'is off-putting to women who might otherwise be interested in pursuing careers in the field.'

Recently the journal *Sky and Telescope*, recognizing that 'Big Bang' has a sexual connotation, ran a competition to find a 'less offensive' but equally graphic term for this event. But in vain. After looking at countless entries, the judges decided that the original had to stay.

Feminism was not always like this. 'Twenty years ago,' says Koertge, 'its dominant mood could have been represented by the Second World War posters of Rosie the Riveter. Activists were rolling up their sleeves and demanding access to traditionally male jobs.

'Women were no longer willing to be nurses or legal secretaries or lab technicians. They wanted to be electricians, engineers, forest rangers and astronauts – and gender stereotypes which implied that women couldn't deal with machines or think analytically were anathema to them.'

But a Rip Van Winkle who fell asleep during the Seventies would be amazed by the changed nature of feminism today. 'The tough and strong-armed Rosie Riveters have been displaced by moralizing Sensitive Susans, each desperately trying to find a new ideological flaw in the so-called "hegemonic discourse of patriarchal, racist, colonial, Eurocentric culture".'

This kind of dogmatic phraseology was typical of the feminists who all too often talked like Communists and Nazis. One example was their argument that belief in logic was a form of insanity. It went like this: Hitler was both logical and insane. Therefore logic is insane.

The history of women's achievements in science often attracted feminist teachers. But students learned little or nothing about Marie Curie, Lise Meitner or Caroline

Herschel. Instead, they would be told of the 'contributions' of the allegedly forgotten healing arts of herbalists and witches. Some observers have likened this to a clash between the male, Apollonian culture of the ancient Greeks and female, Earth Mother cults akin to that of the Maenads.

'The tragedy is that women, already a tiny minority among scientists, could use some support from moderate feminists as they seek to gain acceptance and equal treatment. But instead they find the opposite, because the moderate feminists are not there any more.'

The Paranormal is all Peter Pan

F ew subjects more infuriate scientists, physical scientists in particular, than claims of 'paranormal' events, such as spoon-bending, levitation and communication with the dead.

They are resented because, if confirmed, the whole fabric of science would be threatened. On both sides of the Atlantic, sceptical committees have been set up to investigate such events, and they almost invariably conclude that the claim in question is a fake.

One scientist, Dennis Flanagan, spoke for many when he declared that, after a century of failure to perform paranormal experiments with repeatable results, the subject has become 'a bloody bore'.

Lynn Picknett is an energetic collector of strange folklore with no such inhibitions. She has just published a finely illustrated book on the subject, filled with fascinating and unintentionally hilarious tales. The book's dust-jacket tells us she 'is a leading authority on the paranormal. She writes and broadcasts regularly on the subject . . . She works as a healer.'

If naïve, she is at least honest. She does not hesitate to reveal photographs of mediums caught cheating, or the bogus photographs of fairies that deceived Sir Arthur Conan Doyle. The great difficulty in verifying paranormal claims is that the evidence always proves elusive – such as the photographs of ghosts which are visible only to the ghost-hunter.

Picknett has an excuse for this. She blames it on a

253

personage called the Cosmic Joker, or the god Pan, whose sinister antics gave the word 'panic' to our language. He is a 'cruel, bored god' who amuses himself by revealing proofs of supernatural happenings and then destroying the proofs before they can be examined.

Elsie Wright and Frances Griffith, the two Yorkshire teenagers who faked the pictures which deceived Conan Doyle, were typical victims of the Joker. They could see the fairies, but with terrible unfairness he made them vanish whenever they produced a camera.

Another of his victims was Joseph Smith, founder of the Mormons. The angel Moroni gave him gold and brass plates bearing hieroglyphics, which he translated with the angel's help into the *Book of Mormon*. But Smith's reputation for honesty has suffered ever since, because the angel removed the plates before anyone else could examine them.

This fellow Pan is even wicked enough to swindle hundreds of people out of their worldly possessions. Typically, Picknett says, he informs a trusting cult-leader that the world is about to end in fire, but that if they will sell everything they own and stand on a hilltop, alien spaceships will rescue them before the conflagration. Then, of course, the spaceships fail to turn up.

'History attests the Joker's power,' the author says shudderingly. The Joker loves to arrange tantalizing 'coincidences', a good example being the apparent similarities between the assassinations of American presidents Lincoln and Kennedy. 'It is difficult [in these two assassinations] to escape the notion of the malign influence of the Joker,' Picknett writes.

On the contrary, it is quite easy. She gives the following facts: Lincoln was elected president in 1860 and Kennedy in 1960. A hundred is a remarkable number only because we count in tens. Both men were involved in civil rights. So was nearly every president since Lincoln. Both were assassinated on a Friday and in the presence of their wives. There was a one in forty-nine chance – not remarkably long odds – that both murders should occur on a Friday, and both were on an occasion that wives were likely to attend. Both men were shot in the head. The most logical place for a murderer to aim. Both their successors were called Johnson, were Southern Democrats and were in the Senate. This is less surprising than it sounds. Of the 41 US presidents, 13 have been Democrats, 15 were Southerners and 12 had been Senators. And Johnson is one of the commonest names in America. Of the 8,602 people listed in the current *Who's Who in America*, nearly 4 per cent are Johnsons.

Andrew Johnson was born in 1808, Lyndon in 1908. One assassin was born in 1839, the other in 1939. That 100 again. The names of the assassins each had 15 letters. So did the assassin of President Garfield. So do many people's.

The paranormal is filled with these dubious 'coincidences'. Many people associated with the discovery of Tutankhamun's tomb in 1922 were mysteriously 'struck down', Picknett suggests, by an ancient curse; but this is Hollywood, not history. Today it is commonly accepted that the tomb's discoverers, Lord Carnarvon and Howard Carter, invented the 'curse' to discourage robbers.

Like the writers of many books on the paranormal, Picknett dislikes scepticism. She calls it an 'extreme form of gullibility'. Another paranormalist, in Stalinist style, calls it a 'mental illness'.

But the science writer Arthur C. Clarke takes a more robust view: 'You cannot build an informed democracy out of people who will believe in little green men from Venus. Willingness to accept unsupported statements is the greatest ally of the demagogue and the dictator.'

Get Resurrected with Frank Tipler

I claim that either theology is pure nonsense,
a subject with no content, or else that it must ultimately
become a branch of physics.

Frank Tipler

Tipler has made the most startling prediction since science and religion diverged late in the last century. He believes that everyone who has ever lived will be resurrected and allowed to live out their lives again.

But there is nothing religious about his prediction. Even if somewhat speculative, it is based strictly on science. Its feasibility depends on the findings of future and super-powerful astronomical telescopes. It assumes that the beings who live at a time in the extremely remote future, which he calls 'Omega Point', will be able to resurrect us because they will have almost infinitely powerful computers.

Tipler, professor of mathematical physics at Tulane University, New Orleans, and a former senior research fellow at Oxford, takes the commonly accepted view among physicists that everything that can happen must happen.

'I cannot prove my theory,' he admits, 'and there is at present no way to test it. But it seems absolutely logical, and it is based entirely on our present knowledge. Just as we, out of scientific curiosity, make clumsy and partly successful efforts to recreate the bodies and ways of thought of our pre-human ancestors, so our far future descendants will be immeasurably more successful in recreating us.'

The vastly powerful computers of these beings at Omega Point would be so sensitive that they would be able to look back into their past and extract almost all the information that was there. Yet they will be able to do this only if they can acquire the necessary information. And this, in turn, depends on whether the universe is going to continue to expand for ever – whether it is 'open' – or whether, by contrast, it is 'closed', so that it collapses under its own weight in a 'Big Crunch' some 20,000 million years hence.

Astronomy will eventually give an answer to this long-debated question. The required information will consist of light-rays that we radiate continually into space, and which an infinitely sensitive telescope could capture with 100 per cent accuracy.

'We cannot 'see' a person who lived centuries ago,' Tipler explains, 'because the light rays from that person have long ago left the solar system.' Similarly, if the universe is open, all information about us will ultimately be dissipated and lost for ever. But a very different situation prevails if the universe is closed. All the radiation that has ever been emitted will converge on the Omega Point. 'All the light-rays from the people who died a thousand years ago, from all the people now living, and from all the people who will be living a thousand years hence, will intersect there.'

His colleagues are intrigued, but not entirely convinced. 'It is certainly logical in principle to suggest that an infinite amount of information can be stored in a closed universe,' says Martin Rees (later to become Astronomer Royal). 'But whether it would ever happen in practice is another matter. I would put the theory on the borderline between science and good science fiction.'

Tipler, however, has published a complete description of it in the leading physics journal *Zygon*. Our descendants at

Omega Point, he explains, would have almost infinite energy at their disposal. This would be provided by a phenomenon called 'gravitational shear', which would result from the fact that if the universe collapses it will collapse very unevenly. Mathematical models show it expanding in one direction while contracting in others, a conflict which, according to Einstein's general theory of relativity, would produce a gravitational 'warping' exploitable as a gigantic source of heat and power.

Tipler claims that we will be conscious of being resurrected. 'We will not merely be simulations of people who once existed, like the characters in Shakespeare's historical plays. Otherwise it wouldn't be a perfect simulation. Real people when dramatized make very poor simulations because they do not have free will. If my theory is correct, it implies that when people die, the next thing that they will be conscious of is living again in a future almost unimaginably different from the world in which they died.'

The Saga of Fred Hoyle

The academic world has been once more in a turmoil of anger against a maverick whom many of them see as being to science what the over-talkative former Bishop of Durham was to religion – Professor Sir Fred Hoyle.

Sir Fred, and his mathematical colleague Chandra Wickramasinghe, produced a new bombshell in *Nature* claiming that flu epidemics are caused by sunspots. Their conclusion, which has infuriated medical scientists, is based on their rigidly held belief that space is full of viruses. Storms on the sun's surface (indicated by sunspots) are supposed to drive these viruses into the earth's atmosphere, whereupon we all catch flu.

This claim, that denies all conventional explanations of flu outbreaks, was not exactly new. Some angry scientists have even written a special sub-program in their word processors which, by pressure of a single key, will bring the phrase 'Contrary to the views of Hoyle and Wickramasinghe . . .' to the screen.

For H & W take the provocative view that all life comes from space. Aids, Legionnaires' Disease, the germs that have caused outbreaks of disease throughout history, all come wafting down through the clouds like microscopic little green men. But the real fury arises with their claim that Darwin's theory of evolution by natural selection is wrong, and that evolution occurs because mutating life-forms continually fall from space. Nor, in their view, is this an accident. It was deliberately arranged long ago by a super-intelligent civilization who wished to 'seed' the earth. In pursuit of this case they make claims that their critics consider downright outrageous.

The accusation that has caused the most outrage is that Archaeopteryx, one of the most significant pieces of evidence for natural selection, is a fake. Archaeopteryx was a creature, half reptile, half bird, that lived about 60 million years ago. The fossil of this feathered reptile, one of the prides of the British Museum, shows that the creature was evolving from one species to another without any help from space invasions.

However, this was no problem for H & W. They claimed that the feathers were actually made of concrete and were put there in 1861 by its discoverer, Carl Haeberlein. Their book on the subject provoked a review in the *New Scientist* by the Reading University zoologist Beverly Halstead of unprecedented savagery:

> 'This book is couched in such intemperate language and contains such demonstrable falsehoods, as well as hardly imaginable calumnies of persons unable to defend themselves, that it is exceedingly difficult not to fall into the trap of exploding into an emotional tirade . . .
>
> 'Its main thesis is patently ludicrous and can be proved to be false. We must ask the question: what is this all about? This is the unsavoury aspect, which makes this one of the most despicable pieces of writing it has been my misfortune ever to read. It displays utter contempt for minimal standards of scholarship – the book seems to portray a hatred of Charles Darwin and a most involved and twisted mentality towards zoologists. This libellous nonsense will remain for a long time a stain on the reputations of both authors.'

The museum fraternity were just as angrily pressing the H & W keys on their computers. 'There is not a grain of truth in any of these outrageous allegations,' said Alan Charig, former chief curator at the British Museum.

'Certainly,' said Tom Kemp, curator of the University Museum at Oxford, 'the claim that Archaeopteryx is a fake should be investigated. But the investigation should be done by those who actually understand fossils, not a couple of people who exhibit nothing more than a Gargantuan conceit that they are clever enough to solve other people's problems for them, when they do not even begin to recognize the nature and complexity of those problems.'

Hoyle himself denies writing anything objectionable. 'But we may have included a few mild sarcasms,' he concedes.

The most puzzling part of all this is that, in other branches of science, he is a giant. 'He has made great and fundamental contributions to astronomy,' said Patrick Moore. The most important of these is his discovery, with the American physicist William Fowler, of the way that the heavy chemical elements that fill our bodies, such as oxygen, carbon and iron, are made in the nuclear furnaces of giant stars. Fowler won a Nobel prize for this work, but Hoyle, to his justifiable annoyance, did not.

But even astronomy, at which Hoyle – co-founder of the now discredited Steady State model of the universe – is a top theorist, gave H & W another opportunity for starting a furious quarrel. They accused an American astronomer, J. Mayo Greenberg, of plagiarism. Greenberg developed a theory that space contains 'pre-organic' material, which H & W claim is an unacknowledged copy of their own theory. 'We must congratulate him on his startling accuracy,' they said slyly.

Greenberg reacted like other victims of H & W's 'mild sarcasms'. 'These two men are constantly making these stupid accusations against me,' he retorted. 'I think they have never forgiven me for pointing out some years ago at a public meeting that they had made an elementary scientific error.'

H & W seem to have a genius for annoying people. Whatever the merits of their theories, their rows cause far more enjoyment than the whingeings of bishops.

The Hot Air of Albert Gore

Danger is shining through the sky . . .
We have to tell our children that they must redefine
their relationship to the sky, and they must think of
the sky as a threatening part of the environment.

Albert Gore

When the future Vice-President of the United States gave this terrifying warning in the winter of 1992, he was not thinking of alien invasions or colliding asteroids but of a comparatively minor nuisance, the hole in the Antarctic ozone layer.

Unless drastic action was taken against it, Mr Gore warned, ultraviolet radiation from the Sun would eat up all life. And as an afterthought, if any life survived, the UV radiation would make conditions even more unpleasant for it by rendering the Aids virus more virulent.

Just before becoming Vice President, only a heart-beat from the supreme office, Mr Gore published the widely selling *Earth in the Balance*. Now academics who do not share what one of them calls his 'grim, exaggerated views', have responded with a book of their own: *Environmental Gore*. In this rare book-that-reviews-a-book, they challenge his science and oppose his remedies.*

Environmental Gore: A Constructive Response to 'Earth in the Balance', edited by John A. Baden.

Taking into account not only the ozone hole, but alleged global warming and overpopulation, Mr Gore feels the situation is so serious that it demands a 'Global Marshall Plan' and a world government that would introduce the environmental equivalent of Star Wars.

This would be no *laissez-faire* property-owning democracy. Indeed, it is hard to see how it would differ from a dictatorship.

Childbirth would be restricted. Rigidly centralized bureaucracies would decide what technologies should be permitted, and there would be no appeal against their decisions. Those industrialists who obeyed these orders would have 'guaranteed profits', while those who did not would presumably go bankrupt. Nations that refused to co-operate would have their exports banned.

Nor does he have any time for dissidents, the 'less than reputable' sceptics about global warming, the 'ferocious defenders of waste', the economists who 'ignore bad things', and the 'appeasers', whose complacency about the environment reminds him of Neville Chamberlain's relaxed attitude to Hitler.

The most frightening aspect of Mr Gore's book, says one of these authors, 'is the utter intolerance towards those who disagree with him. [He sees them as] not simply as wrong but ill. Dr Gore knows what is best for his patients and is ready to administer his medicine.'

Central to his theme are his strange views of the relationship between man and nature. He vilifies Francis Bacon, the great seventeenth-century philosophical advocate of science-based wealth who declared: 'Man conquers nature by obeying her.' Mr Gore seems only to have understood the first three words of this sentence; man's supposed conquest of nature makes him think of Mussolini's ruthless Italian campaign against Abyssinia with poison gas.

Bacon's point is too subtle for him, for he summarizes it with exactly the opposite of its true meaning: 'The new power derived from scientific knowledge could be used to dominate nature with moral impunity.'

What are the chances that Mr Gore might get into the White House and be in a position to put his programme into action? I received an alarming message on the Internet from the space expert James Oberg, who said that Mr Gore was negotiating with Nasa for a ride in the space shuttle in Election Year 1996.

By this he would upstage Mr Clinton and perhaps gain the Democratic nomination. But happily, on telephoning Mr Oberg, I discovered that his message was an April Fool.

Bow Down to the Cosmic Lords

The Master Aetherius, who reigns on the planet Venus will soon come down to earth. His strength will be greater than all the armies of the world, and those with a 'negative' attitude to him will be 'removed'.

This astonishing message was conveyed to a packed and fervent public meeting which I attended. Flying saucers, filled either with the servants, or else the robots of this terrible being, apparently visit the Earth regularly to prepare for his coming, as they have done for the last 50,000 years. But now, we were assured, a New Age has begun, and his arrival is imminent.

During eight hours of speeches, in a London hotel, about 300 members of the Aetherius Society were repeatedly told two things about these flying saucers. They are real and friendly, but there is an inter-governmental plot to conceal their existence.

These facts were 'the single most important issue facing mankind today'. John Holder, who holds a decorate in bio-chemistry from Hull University and who works as a unit trust manager, set out the scientific 'proof' of the existence of the spacefaring minions of Aetherius.

His proof consisted largely of numbers. An incident in which a Japan Air Lines Jet had been 'bugged' by a mysterious object while flying over Alaska had generated 329 pages of official documents. Norad, the US Air Defence Command, had collected data on 'no less that ten million incidents' during the past 20 years. The British Ministry of

Defence had records of 2,250 sightings over four years, and 15,000 of them since 1962.

To Richard Lawrence, secretary of the Society's European headquarters, these numbers proved a great deal. These aerial activities were caused, not only by Aetherius, but by the other 'Cosmic Lords'.

It appears that every planet in our Solar System is inhabited by these beings. The fact that space probes had found all these planets to be uninhabitable did not matter, since the Cosmic Lords consisted of pure mind. They had no bodies that would suffer from poisonous atmospheres.

The true facts about their existence had now been 'revealed'. Revealed to whom? To their prophet on Earth, a resident of America. His Eminence Sir George King, who has inherited his knighthood from a Byzantine emperor. Sir George became advanced in the science of yoga, which in his case meant communing with God. Back in 1954, he 'heard a voice'.

'Do not smirk,' said Mr Lawrence sternly. 'St Paul also heard a voice. So did the prophet Elijah.' He explained that Sir George had received more than 600 messages from the Cosmic Lords, and they had appointed him the representative of their Planetary Parliament. Sir George is now the medium through which the Cosmic Lords speak to the people of Earth. His is the voice but theirs are the words. To let us hear them, Mr Lawrence played three unintelligible tapes. I checked an impulse to laugh as he warned: 'We regard these transmissions as extremely holy.'

It was depressing to listen to this farrago of nonsense. The meeting had started in a fairly scientific manner, but as it proceeded the tone grew progressively more evangelical and intolerant. 'Patrick Moore doesn't believe in flying saucers, but he's discredited,' Lawrence declared. The audience never laughed. In later meetings of the Society, Lawrence and his colleagues claimed that the dimensions of the Egyptian pyramids reveal the precise distance between the Earth and the Sun, data which their builders could not possibly have known, but which the Cosmic Lords could have fed into their minds.

Lawrence again poured scorn on the 'debunkers'. 'Some people have such closed minds. They wouldn't even recognize a flying saucer if it landed.' In this he is wrong. That is about the only circumstance in which we would recognize it. It is the absence of any artifacts that makes it impossible to take these people seriously.

Part Six

TEST YOUR

KNOWLEDGE

How much science do you know? Here is a selection of my Christmas Science Quizzes to test your knowledge. Answers are given at the end of the section. Needless to say, the £400 and £450 prizes for the answers to specially difficult questions are no longer on offer!

Quiz No. 1

1. Who said:
(a) 'Mighty are numbers, joined with art resistless.'
(b) 'A machine may not harm humanity or, through inaction, allow humanity to come to harm.'
(c) 'What of Lavoisier, noisy father of all noisy discoveries? He has no ideas of his own, so he appropriates those of others.'
(d) 'If your theory is found to be against the Second Law of Thermodynamics I can give you no hope; there is nothing for it but to collapse in deepest humiliation.'
(e) 'Scientists imagine they are the brains of the nation. Actually, they are not the brains but the shit.'
(f) 'Look at the morning star as it sets majestically on the breast of the infinite. Melancholy will overcome you. No one can resist the melancholy in nature.'
(g) 'The danger already exists that mathematicians have made a covenant with the Devil to darken the spirit and confine man in the bonds of Hell.'
(h) 'The history of England is emphatically the history of progress.'
(i) 'It is more important that a proposition be interesting than that it be true.'
(j) 'I'm as drunk a lord, but then I am one, so what does it matter?'

2. Are the following true or false?
(a) The globular star clusters are among the youngest objects in the universe
(b) The Star of Bethlehem is now believed to have been Halley's Comet
(c) Sir William Herschel was a pioneer in fingerprinting
(d) Ophiuchus is one of the constellations of the Zodiac

3. Nine duchesses argue about who should sit next to whom at a single conference table with numbered seats. How many possible seating arrangements could they choose?
(a) 9
(b) 18
(c) 36
(d) 81
(e) 729
(f) 362,880

4. What were the Seven Sciences?

5. [A special question that originally carried a £400 prize.] The following 75-digit number is a 'prime product', consisting of 2 prime numbers multiplied together (prime numbers are divisible only by themselves and 1). Find the 2 prime numbers:

297, 426, 271, 865, 197,
115, 769, 312, 409, 175,
873, 555, 265, 022, 587,
277, 069, 502, 757, 095,
321, 297, 480, 347, 763

6. What is the following sentence an example of? 'I met a man in Oregon who hadn't any teeth – yet that man could play on the bass drum better than any man I ever met.'

7. Prove that the Beast of Revelations is a fox.

8. Who attacked Copernicus's model of the solar system as being 'anti-Biblical and intolerable'?

9. What is the nearest star to the Earth?

10. What information are these sayings meant to remind us of?
(a) 'Oh, be a fine girl, kiss me right now!'
(b) 'How I need a drink, alcoholic of course, after that long lecture involving quantum mechanics.'

11. Where would one expect to find high concentrations of the elements titanium, vanadium, chromium, manganese, iron, cobalt and nickel?

12. What is starry-gazy pie?

13. In warfare, why were tanks so-named?

14. What are, or were, the following:
(a) mascons   (b) neutrinos   (c) porphyrin
(d) airglow   (e) the Kirkwood gaps (f) anti-hydrogen
(g) tachyons   (h) black dwarves   (i) velociraptors
(j) echo-location   (k) a steganogram

15. For what have the following been in the scientific news?
(a) Thomas Ayres   (b) Mark Abrahams   (c) Paul Horowitz
(d) Colin Humphreys   (e) Warwick Collins (f) Kathy Thornton
(g) Marek Abramowicz (h) Tim Severin

16. Who used to be called 'Mr Tripos'?

Quiz No. 2

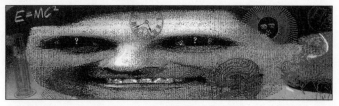

1. Who said:

(a) 'Aristotle maintained that women have fewer teeth than men. Although he was twice married, it never occurred to him to verify this statement by examining his wives' mouth.'

(b) 'Psychologists are no more scientists than converted savages are Christians.'

(c) 'Space travel is utter bilge.'

(d) 'My rule was simple – each man should know everything he needed to know for his job, and nothing else.'

(e) 'Those hateful persons called Original Researchers.'

(f) 'Anyone who can be replaced by a machine deserves to be.'

(g) ' I'd lay down my life for two brothers or eight cousins.'

(h) 'No country without an atomic bomb can properly consider itself independent.'

(i) 'Scientists are treacherous allies on committees, for they can change their minds in response to arguments.'

(j) 'Books must follow sciences, and not sciences books.'

(k) 'There is no democracy in physics. We can't say that some second-rate guy has as much right to his opinion as Fermi.'

2. Why is a recent estimate that the universe is less than 12 billion years old almost certainly wrong?

3. Of what invention did Stalin say: 'It will unmake our work. No greater instrument of counter-revolution and conspiracy can be imagined.'?

4. In the once fashionable temperature scale invented by René Réaumur, what was the boiling point of water?

5. For thousands of years there have been man-made sonic booms. How were they caused?

6. Solve the equation:

$$\frac{A^3}{B^3} + \frac{C^3}{D^3} = 6$$

where A, B, C and D are all positive whole numbers below 100.

7. From where did Napoleon get the inspiration to build the Arc de Triomphe in Paris?

8. What are the latitudes of the Tropics of Cancer and Capricorn?

9. Just as foxhounds make a 'pack', what is the collective name for:
(a) owls (b) ravens (c) larks (d) vipers (e) rats (f) rhinoceroses (g) elks
(h) mussels (i) monkeys (j) goldfish (k) caterpillars (l) falcons?

10. Where was the city of Pelusium?

11. In industry, what is carbon monoxide commonly used for?

12. What made the mathematician Srinivasa Ramanujan call 1,729 one of the most interesting numbers he knew?

13. How do Loughborough University scientists propose to alleviate the ever increasing growth of the air passenger market?

14. Where, in Europe, would one be most likely to find the fossils of velociraptors?

15. Where does Dactyl dance with Ida?

16. In Royal Naval ships, why are the dog watches so-called?

17. What problem did Archimedes solve that inspired him to rush naked into the street shouting 'Eureka!'?

18. A giant star about 10,000 light-years from Earth is tearing itself to pieces. What is it called?

19. What was Isaac Asimov's Zeroth Law of Robotics?

20. How many years does energy generated in the Sun's core take to reach its surface:
(a) 1 (b) 5 (c) 100 (d) 10,000 (e) 1 million (f) 100 million?

21. What, in geology and Earth science, is:
(a) a coombe (b) a monadnock (c) a neck (d) a tombolo (e) a jehel
(f) a nunatak (g) a literol (h) a cordillera (i) fool's gold?

22. Why are the noble gases so-called?

23. Who used electricity to demonstrate the behaviour of muscles in a frog's legs?

24. What was the dogma of the Soviet charlatan Trofim Lysenko?

25. What have scientists been searching for near the south pole of the Moon?

26. Why is the American space shuttle Endeavour spelled in the English way?

Quiz No.3

$$V_0 = V_0 (1 + \alpha t) \frac{}{H_0 + h},$$

$$1 + \frac{h}{H_0} = 1 + \alpha t;$$

$$\frac{h}{H_0} = \alpha t,$$

1. Who said:

(a) 'I don't want to belong to any club that will have me as a member.'

(b) 'There is no evil in the atom, only in men's souls.'

(c) 'We are all agreed that your theory is crazy. The question which divides us is whether it is crazy enough to have a chance of being correct.'

(d) 'That an opinion has been widely held is no evidence that it is not utterly absurd.'

(e) 'The whole aim of practical politics is to keep the populace alarmed (and hence clamorous to be led to safety) by menacing it with an endless series of hobgoblins, all of them imaginary.'

(f) 'The fossilized bones of an ape more manlike, or a man more apelike, than any yet known may await some unborn palaeontologist.'

(g) 'The more I read about Socrates the less I wonder that they poisoned him.'

(h) 'Earth is the cradle of mankind, but one cannot stay in the cradle for ever.'

(i) 'I would rather believe that Yankee professors lie than that stones fall from Heaven.'

(j) 'Prometheus reaches for the stars with an insane grin on his face and a totem-symbol in his hand.'

(k) 'The first invention of a super-intelligent machine will be the last invention that mankind is allowed to make.'

2. A minister was sacked by his ruler for 'introducing infinitesimals into administration.' (a) Who was he? (b) Who sacked him?

3. (a) What is sapa? (b) Give at least one of the two reasons why Roman prostitutes ate it neat?

4. The world's potentially most valuable substance costs an estimated $300 billion per milligram. What is it?

5. The following pieces of vile English are cryptograms in 'bureaucratese'. Give their better known originals:

(a) 'In the case of the ruler, it might be considered appropriate, from a moral or ethical point of view, to yield up to that potentate all of those goods and materials of whatever character or quality which can be shown to have had their original source in any portion of the domain of the latter.'

(b) 'I repeat; for the gift or loan of a quadrupedal transportive graminivore, I would be willing to donate the substance of my estate in its entirety.'

(c) 'I am not what might be called an adept in the art of public speaking, the opposite of which might be fairly stated of my opponent in this debate.'

(d) 'Objective consideration of contemporary phenomena compels the conclusion that success or failure in competitive activities exhibits no tendency to be commensurate with innate capacity, but that a considerable element of the unpredictable must invariably be taken into account.'

6. [This question originally carried an extra prize of £450.] The following four pairs of numbers are 'consecutive prime pairs'. That is, they are prime numbers separated only by 2, and which do not have any other prime pairs between them:

3 and 5; 5 and 7; 11 and 13; 17 and 19.

What is the first group of **five** consecutive prime pairs?

7. What do 2,3,7,8-tetrach lorodibenzo-p-dioxin and ethyl S-2-diisoprovy laminoethylmethyl phosphonothiolate have in common?

8. What are the familiar names of the following stars:
(a) Alpha Eridani
(b) Alpha Centauri
(c) Alpha Canis Majoris
(d) Alpha Orionis
(e) Beta Persei
(f) Alpha Tauri
(g) Zeta Ursae Majoris
(h) Alpha Ursae Minoris
(i) Beta Geminorum
(j) Eta Tauri.

9. What phenomenon was Bertrand Russell describing when he quoted these lines from *Alice Through the Looking Glass*:

But I was thinking of a plan
To dye one's whiskers green,
And always use so large a fan
That they could not be seen.

10. Which famous scientist concealed his identity from the Nazis under the name of 'Dr Moore'?

11. Who was the only scientist to have been expelled from the Royal Society of London for infamous conduct?

12. Who invented the terms (a) black hole and (b) Big Bang?

13. What approximate percentage of the atmosphere consists of:

(a) carbon dioxide (b) carbon monoxide (c) nitrogen (d) oxygen
(e) ozone (f) methane (g) man-made CFCs?

14. What people inspired Shakespeare's creation of Caliban in *The Tempest*?

15. What two bodies in the solar system are in a 'double tidal lock'?

16. Why is the largest crater on the Martian moon Phobos named 'Stickney'?

17. Thirty-six passengers were killed when the airship Hindenburg was destroyed by fire in 1937. How many survived?

18. Europe's Soho spacecraft, designed to examine the Sun, is on its way to an orbit called L2. What does the L stand for?

19. Why did Napoleon send the message to Josephine: 'Don't wash, I am coming home!'

20. (a) Where, and (b) how high above sea-level, is the world's highest mountain-top astronomical observatory?

21. What action did the Astronomer Royal John Flamsteed take when Isaac Newton and Edmund Halley published his half-written star catalogue without authorization?

Answers to Quizzes

QUIZ NO. 1

1. (a) Euripides (b) Isaac Asimov (c) Jean-Paul Marat
(d) Arthur Eddington (e) Lenin (f) Napoleon (g) St Augustine
(h) Macaulay (i) Alfred North Whitehead (j) Bertrand Russell

2. (a) false (b) false (c) true (d) true

3. (f) 362,880

4. In the Middle Ages, there were four sciences in the Quadrivium: arithmetic, music, geometry and astronomy; together with three of the Trivium: grammar, rhetoric and logic

5. The two primes are:

730, 141, 588, 155, 644,
511, 360, 779, 722, 065,
841

and

407, 354, 240, 177, 584,
110, 037, 203, 671, 316,
079, 261, 132, 643

6. A non-sequitur

7. Arrange the numbers and letters thus:

1	2	3	4	5	**6**	7	8	9
A	B	C	D	E	**F**	G	H	I
J	K	L	M	N	**O**	P	Q	R
S	T	U	V	W	**X**	Y	Z	

and read the three letters below 6

8. Martin Luther

9. The Sun

10. (a) the spectra of the stars (b) the first 15 digits of pi, recorded by the length of each word

11. In the core of a supernova, just before its explosion

12. An old Cornish dish of herrings baked in a pie with their heads poking through the crust

13. 'Tank' was a First World War code to avoid arousing German suspicions

14. (a) mass concentrations on a planet's surface
(b) particles with no charge and almost no mass
(c) the compound that makes blood red
(d) nocturnal luminescence caused by the presence of atomic oxygen
(e) regions in the Asteroid Belt where no asteroids are to be found
(f) hydrogen made of anti-matter
(g) theoretical faster-than-light particles
(h) relics of stars whose nuclear reactions have ceased
(i) aggressive, carnivorous dinosaurs
(j) the ability of submarines – and some animals – to 'see' by detecting echoes
(k) a message which conceals a secret, second message

15. (a) finding a super-violent flare on a Sun-like star
(b) chairing the awards of the Ig Nobel prizes
(c) finding 37 unexplained radio signals from nearby stars
(d) his announcement of new materials that will transform economic life
(e) predicting that advanced computer networks will behave aggressively
(f) helping to repair the Hubble Space Telescope
(g) predicting that a corridor near a black hole can be curved and straight at the same time
(h) trying to prove that Polynesians could have colonized the Americas

16. The scholar seated on a three-legged stool who disputed in the Cambridge Philosophy School on Ash Wednesdays

QUIZ NO. 2

1. (a) Bertrand Russell (b) Georges Politzer (c) Astronomer Royal Sir Richard Woolley (d) General Leslie Groves, officer commanding the atomic bomb-building project (e) James Barrie (f) Dennis Gunton (g) J.B.S. Haldane (h) Charles de Gaulle (i) Maurice Bowra (j) Francis Bacon (k) Luis Alvarez

2. Because the universe contains stars that are more than 15 billion years old

3. The telephone

4. 80

5. The cracking of a whip

6. The solution to the equation is:
   A=17, B=21, C=37 and D=21

The clue is that B and D must be equal. A computer program can then be run, like this one in BASIC:
   10 FOR A= 1 to 100
   20 FOR C= 1 to 100
   30 FOR D= 1 to 100
   40 B=D
   50 IF A^3+C^3=6*D^3 THEN PRINT A,B,C,D: END
   60 NEXT: NEXT: NEXT

7. From the south gate of Karnak in Egypt

8. 23 27' north and 23 27' south

9. (a) a parliament of owls (b) an unkindness of ravens (c) an exaltation of larks (d) a den or nest of vipers (e) a colony of rats (f) a crash of rhinoceroses (g) a gang of elks (h) a bed of mussels (i) a troop of monkeys (j) a troubling of goldfish (k) an army of caterpillars (l) a cast of falcons

10. In ancient Egypt, near what is now Port Said

11. For purifying metals, a 'reducing agent'

12. 1,729 is the smallest number that can be expressed as the sum of two cubes in two ways. It is 1 cubed+12 cubed and 9 cubed+10 cubed

13. By making aircraft fly in formation

14. European velociraptor fossils are most likely to be found in the Isle of Wight

15. In space: Ida is an asteroid and Dactyl its moon

16. 'Dog' watch is a corruption of 'dodge'. It prevents the same men being on duty together each day

17. By immersing a gold crown in his bath, Archimedes had found that it had been fraudulently alloyed with silver, thereby establishing the law of buoyancy

18. The star Eta Carinae

19. 'A robot may not harm humanity or, through inaction, allow humanity to come to harm.' The plot of *Prelude to Foundation* would not have worked without it

20. It takes a million years for energy generated in the Sun's core to reach its surface

21. (a) a short valley into a hillside (b) an isolated hill or rock

(c) a volcanic plug (d) a bar connecting an island with the mainland
(e) a mountain range (f) a peak projecting through an ice peak
(g) that part of the sea shore between high and low tide
(h) parallel ranges (i) iron pyrites

22. Noble gases are supposedly too aristocratic to form compounds with the common herd of elements

23. Luigi Galvani

24. Lysenko claimed that acquired characteristics in wheat could be inherited

25. Craters filled with ice, which would be invaluable to lunar colonists

26. It is named after the first ship commanded by Captain Cook

QUIZ NO. 3

1. (a) Groucho Marx (b) Adlai Stevenson (c) Neils Bohr (d) Bertrand Russell (e) H.L. Mencken (f) Thomas Huxley (g) Thomas Macaulay (h) Konstantin Tsiolkovski (i) President Thomas Jefferson (j) Arthur Koestler (k) Arthur C. Clarke

2. (a) Pierre Simon, Marquis de Laplace (b) Napoleon

3. (a) Sapa is a strong artificial sweetener made from boiled wine (b) It gave women attractive pale complexions and was believed to cause abortions

4. Anti-matter, the ideal fuel for starships

5. (a) 'Render unto Caesar the things that are Caesar's' – St Matthew 22:21
(b) 'A horse A horse! My kingdom for a horse!' – Richard III, Act V, sc. iv.
(c) 'I am no orator as Brutus is.' – Julius Caesar, Act III, sc. ii
(d) 'I returned and saw under the sun, that the race is not yet to the swift, nor the battle to the strong, neither yet bread to the wise, nor yet riches to men of understanding, nor yet favour to men of skill, but time and chance happeneth to them all.' – Ecclesiastes, 9:11

6. 909,287 and 909,289; 909,299 and 909,301; 909,317 and 909,319; 909,329 and 909,331; 909,341 and 909,343

7. They are both deadly poisons, respectively known as TCDD and VX

8. (a) Achenar (b) Rigil Kent (c) Sirius (d) Betelgeuse (e) Algol
(f) Aldebaran (g) Mizar (h) Polaris the Pole Star (i) Pollux (j) Alcyone (the brightest star in the Pleiades)

9. The ether wind, which defied all attempts to measure it and which was shown not to exist

10. Albert Einstein

11. The geologist Rudolph Raspe, for plundering an art collection

12. (a) John A. Wheeler (b) Sir Fred Hoyle

13. (a) carbon dioxide 0.034 (b) carbon monoxide 0.00002
(c) nitrogen 77 (d) oxygen 20 (e) ozone 0.000003 (f) methane 0.0001
(g) man-made CFCs 0.000000008

14. The natives of Patagonia, discovered by Magellan

15. Pluto and its moon Charon. One side of each permanently faces the other

16. Crater Stickney on Phobos was named after the wife of the astronomer Asaph Hall, who in 1877 encouraged him in his difficult search for the Martian moons

17. Fifty-six passengers survived the Hindenburg disaster

18. For Joseph, Comte de Lagrange

19. Napoleon was sexually aroused by Josephine's personal odour

20. (a) The world's highest mountain-top astronomical observatory is the Denver High Altitude Observatory at Boulder, Colorado (b) It is, at 4,297 metres, slightly higher than Mauna Kea, Hawaii

21. Flamsteed obtained all the copies of his catalogue that he could and burned them in public

Index